SRA Art Connections

Art Across the Curriculum

Level 2

SRA McGraw-Hill

Columbus, Ohio

A Division of The McGraw-Hill Companies

SRA/McGraw-Hill

A Division of The McGraw·Hill Companies

Copyright © 1998 by SRA/McGraw-Hill.

Printed in the United States of America.

Send all inquiries to:
SRA/McGraw-Hill
250 Old Wilson Bridge Road
Suite 310
Worthington, Ohio 43085

ISBN 0-02-688334-1
1 2 3 4 5 6 7 8 9 PAT 01 00 99 98 97

Table of
Contents

Introduction

What Is *Art Across the Curriculum?*

Art Across the Curriculum is a series of activities designed to help you connect the principles of visual art with other subject areas, so students can understand
- that art touches and shapes their lives in ways they might never have imagined,
- and that the arts and sciences are not separate entities.

Art Connections focuses on the basic elements and principles of art, such as line, shape, form, color, emphasis, unity, balance, and texture. *Art Across the Curriculum* works with these basic principles and relates them specifically to **reading/language arts, mathematics, science, social studies,** the other fine arts **(dance, music, theater),** and **technology.**

Each *Art Across the Curriculum* resource book provides a blackline master in each of six curriculum areas for each lesson in the Student Edition of the **Art Connections** program. The lessons are divided into six units of six lessons each, giving you 216 blackline masters for individual and cooperative experiences. Each blackline master is based on curriculum area objectives that are common throughout the country, including those of individual schools, school districts, states, and curriculum area organizations. These objectives are clearly stated at the bottom of each blackline master.

How Do *Art Across the Curriculum* Activities Relate to Art?

The activities in *Art Across the Curriculum* are connected in several ways to the art lessons in **Art Connections.** Often, they extend the specific concept presented in the lesson. For example, geometric figures in art are related directly to geometric figures in mathematics. The activities sometimes spring from the content of the artwork. For instance, Ben Jones's *King Family* is a natural part of a study on Martin Luther King, Jr., and the contributions he and his family have made to our society.

How Do I Use *Art Across the Curriculum?*

The *Art Across the Curriculum* activities are designed to be used in at least two ways:
- to extend the art lesson into other subject areas. In this case, you can review the activities that go with the art lesson and choose one or more to assign. You may use any or all of the blackline masters during your study of a particular element or principle. Generally, you will want to use them in the week in which you present the primary lesson.
- to introduce an art lesson. In this case, you can review the activities in *Art Across the Curriculum* index in the Teacher Edition to find activities that complement what you are already teaching and introduce the corresponding **Art Connections** lesson through the subject area.

The *Art Across the Curriculum* blackline masters will help you tie basic art principles and elements to all areas of the students' lives.

The Reading/Language Arts Connections

How Do Reading/Language Arts and Visual Art Compare?
The elements and principles of art, such as line, shape, form, color, emphasis, unity, balance, and texture, are also extremely important elements of language. As we write, we endeavor to express our ideas as clearly and precisely as possible. In this attempt, we learn the form, unity, and balance of our language. As we write and speak, we add action, description, and feeling (correlating to line, shape, texture, and color in art) to achieve balance and to create emphasis.

What Do the Reading/Language Arts Activities Cover?
The activities in the reading/language arts category of *Art Across the Curriculum* provide opportunities for using language and extending language experiences while relating to the elements, principles, and subject matter of the art. Through the many activities afforded in these blackline masters, the students will
• develop vocabulary.
• record ideas and feelings.
• develop organizational and writing skills.
• distinguish between fact and opinion.
• use descriptive words.
• become familiar with a variety of genres.
• make comparisons.
• predict outcomes.
• make inferences.
• develop their skills in usage and grammar.
• acquire skills in writing for a variety of purposes.

How Do the Reading/Language Arts Activities Relate to the *Art Connections* Lessons?
The Reading/Language Arts activities are related to the art lessons in a variety of ways:
• the art stimulates writing.
• the art serves as a source for developing vocabulary and literary techniques, such as metaphor, synonyms, compounds, comparison, and exaggeration.
• the art provides ideas for descriptive words.
• the lesson subject matter serves as a springboard for gathering and analyzing information.

The Mathematics Connections

How Do Mathematics and Visual Art Compare?
We often think of mathematics and art as unrelated. However, art is one way to show mathematical principles, and many of the principles of art are mathematical. For example, we can draw pictures of most math problems. In addition, line, shape, and form are an integral part of mathematics.

What Do the Mathematics Activities Cover?
The activities in the mathematics category of *Art Across the Curriculum* cover such skills and concepts as
• patterning,
• critical attributes of geometric shapes and solids,
• number,
• mathematical operations,
• ratio,
• probability,
• graphing,
• measurement,
• problem solving,
• reasoning.

How Do the Mathematics Activities Relate to the *Art Connections* Lessons?
The mathematics activities provided in *Art Across the Curriculum* relate to the art lessons in a variety of ways:
• the art provides opportunities for describing attributes.
• the art serves as a source for identifying geometric shapes and forms.
• the art affords opportunities for problem solving and using mathematical operations.
• the art launches graphing and charting activities.

The Science Connections

How Do Science and Visual Art Compare?

Artists do think like scientists in many ways. They study nature as carefully as scientists—sometimes from the same perspective, sometimes from a different one. When the students are studying a landscape or a still life in **Art Connections,** for example, they must look at the objects scientifically. They will notice that artists are sometimes quite precise and objective in their representation of a natural object or phenomenon; other times artists are more concerned with creating an impression or feeling associated with the natural object. In any case, a good artist uses scientific principles in the work of art.

Art has been a major means of expression and communication since humans have been on Earth. It is likely that art was used before or at least in connection with the development of a language system. We have always used art to describe elements in nature, to record our scientific observations, and to express our ideas and feelings.

Many of the artworks people have created involve nature in some way. Although these portrayals are not always realistic, they are based on scientific reality, our beliefs of reality, and our interpretation of it. Relating science and art is, therefore, a perfect opportunity to develop students' understanding of the connections in our world.

What Do the Science Activities Cover?

The activities included in *Art Across the Curriculum* often spring from the subject of the artwork. Art is a natural way to lead into

- the effects of industry on our environment,
- characteristics of organisms,
- structures of life,
- behavior,
- change ,
- properties of matter,
- observation,
- scientific method,
- interpreting and analyzing data,
- the effects of external stimuli on nature, energy, force, and motion.

How Do the Science Activities Relate to the *Art Connections* Lessons?

Many of the science activities spring from examining the artwork. For example,

- the artwork can lead students into the properties of the artists' media.
- the students might examine the plants and animals in an ecosystem depicted in the art.
- earth science and astronomy activities relate to phenomena exemplified in a work of art.

The Social Studies Connections

How Do Social Studies and Visual Art Compare?

Many of the disciplines of art are also disciplines of the social studies: history and culture, production, perception, criticism, and expression. One of the major goals of many artists is expressing the social issues and the culture of a society. This is also a primary concern of social scientists. The social scientist is also concerned with emphasis, unity, balance, and harmony as principles that influence the success of a society.

What Do the Social Studies Activities Cover?

The social studies activities in *Art Across the Curriculum* provide opportunities for you to introduce and incorporate many skills and concepts. Some of the objectives covered in these activities include
- mapping, graphing, and charting information,
- economic influences and developments,
- business principles,
- technological development,
- history,
- geography,
- social relationships,
- cultural contributions,
- environmental impact,
- and analyzing and interpreting information.

How Do the Social Studies Activities Relate to the *Art Connections* Lessons?

Because artworks are an expression of culture, the art lesson and the social studies activities are related in a variety of ways:
- the art and the subject matter stimulate the study of a variety of cultures,
- the art and the subject matter serve as a source for developing concepts in history, geography, politics, and sociology.
- the principles and elements of art relate harmony and values to harmony and values in societies and cultures.

The Arts Connections

How Do the Arts and Visual Art Compare?

We generally consider artists to be those who express themselves through art, dance, music, and the theater, so the connections among these areas are more immediately obvious than the connections to other disciplines. The elements and principles of dance, music, and theater are basically the same as those of art—line, shape, form, color, emphasis, unity, balance, and texture.

What Do the Arts Activities Cover?

The arts activities in *Art Across the Curriculum* include a variety of music, dance, and theatrical experiences. For example, students

- transfer spatial patterns from the visual to the kinesthetic,
- develop spatial awareness and control,
- interpret works of art in music, dance, and drama,
- reproduce an artwork dramatically, incorporating scenery, costumes, emotions, and dialogue,
- develop an appreciation of a variety of cultures to all areas of the arts,
- use dance, music, and drama to express feelings and ideas.

How Do the Arts Activities Relate to the *Art Connections* Lessons?

The ties among the arts are quite strong. For example,

- while studying the artist's use of texture in their **Art Connections** lesson, students can easily see the connections to texture in music, dance, and theater. In these areas, texture is developed by variation in style, movement, and intensity.
- artworks will inspire interpretation through music, dance, and theater.
- the subject of a work of art leads to comparable representations in music, song, movement, character, setting, and story.

The Technology Connections

How Do Computer Technology and Visual Art Compare?
The computer opens a new world for artists. Not only is it a new medium for expression, it also gives the artist a different way to combine the elements of art. More and more, we are seeing the computer as a tool for producing, manipulating, and viewing graphics.

What Application Should I Use?
The activities in the technology section of *Art Across the Curriculum* were designed for use with Davidson's ***Multimedia Workshop*** but will work with most drawing and painting programs. Depending on your computer and software, you will find some minor differences in specifics. For example, the drawing tool on your software might look different than the one used on these blackline masters. We use a wide paintbrush. Your software might use a pencil or a narrow brush. The students will probably adapt to these differences without any difficulty.

What Computer Basic Do Students Need?
Students need at least one introductory computer lesson before they begin any of these activities. They should receive basic instruction on opening, closing, and saving files, as well as clicking and dragging objects. They should become familiar with the basic use of tools and menu commands. Students might need guidance and further instruction during each lesson.

What Do the Technology Activities Cover?
The technology activities provide a wide variety of experiences that encourage students to
- learn the basic techniques for using drawing and painting programs, such as clicking and dragging, copying, pasting, moving, and manipulating.
- discover that there are many ways to accomplish most tasks.
- sketch and draw.
- practice techniques that simulate watercolor, oil, airbrush, and chalk.
- manipulate text and graphs to create multimedia presentations.

The lessons are independent of each other. Students do not need to complete all of the earlier lessons in order to understand instructions in the later lessons. Some of the lessons are shorter than others, so you might want to have students work on more than one lesson in a given session.

How Do the Technology Activities Relate to the *Art Connections* Lessons?
The technology activities give students a different medium for experimenting with the principles and techniques presented in their **Art Connections** lessons. For example,
- the techniques used in the artworks can often be translated to drawing and painting on the computer. There are limitations, however. Forms and texture, for instance, cannot be created on the computer; they can only be represented.
- the subject of a work of art provides an opportunity for students to interpret the subject in their own way.

*Name*_____ *Date*_____

WORDS ABOUT LINES

Lines are named for the direction in which they move. Here are some words that tell about lines.

horizontal   A horizontal line is flat.
vertical   A vertical line is straight up and down.
diagonal   A diagonal line slants.
zigzag   A zigzag line goes back and forth.

WHAT TO DO: Using the words above, tell which kind of line you would use to draw a picture of these objects.

1. a lightning bolt _____

2. a flagpole _____

3. the top of a table _____

4. the side of a triangle _____

Now, write a sentence using one of the four words above. Use the sample sentence to help you.

Sample sentence: Use <u>vertical</u> lines to draw a flagpole.

Your sentence: _____

Reading/Language Arts Objectives: The student acquires automatic recognition of words through multiple opportunities to read and reread; The student develops vocabulary (word meanings) through reading.

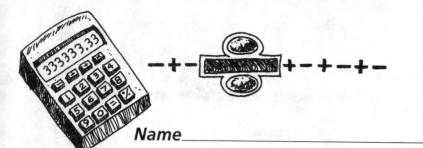

Name_____ Date_____

ABOUT SHAPES

Artists often use different shapes to make patterns or to decorate their art. Here are some common shapes.

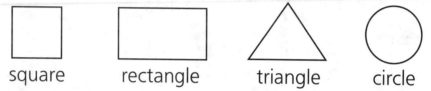

square   rectangle   triangle   circle

WHAT TO DO: Think about the kinds of lines that make each shape. Write the names of the lines in the blanks. Choose vertical, horizontal, diagonal, or curved.

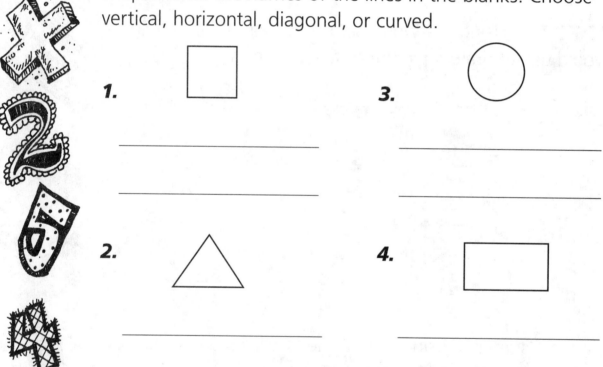

1.

_____

_____

3.

_____

_____

2.

_____

_____

4.

_____

_____

Now, look at the sculpture of the Mexican church. Trace the shapes you find with your finger. Put an **X** next to the shapes you find.

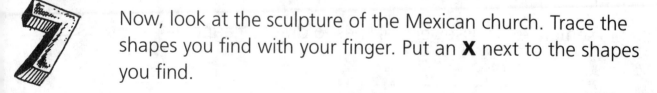

square_____   rectangle _____

circle _____   triangle _____

Mathematics Objective: The student identifies attributes of shapes and solids.

2

Name _____ **Date** _____

HEAT CAUSES CHANGE

The sculpture of the Mexican church is made from clay. Soft clay can be made into different shapes. When the clay is just the right shape, it is heated in an oven called a *kiln*. The heat hardens the clay. Heat causes other things to change, too.

WHAT TO DO: Think about how heat changes water. Use these temperature facts to answer the questions below.

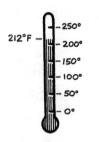

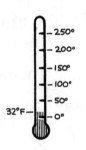

SCIENCE

Water boils at 212°Fahrenheit (100°Centigrade).
Water freezes at 32°Fahrenheit (0°Centigrade).

Does the temperature have to go up or down to freeze water? Write **up** or **down** next to each temperature.

1. 212°F _____ **2.** 10°F _____ **3.** 98°F _____

Does the temperature have to go up or down to boil water? Write **up** or **down** next to each temperature.

4. 10°F _____ **5.** 250°F _____ **6.** 200°F _____

Science Objective: The student manipulates sources of heat to cause change.

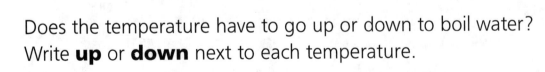

Name_____ Date_____

WHERE IS MEXICO?

The sculpture *Church* was made in the country of Mexico.
Learn how to find places.

WHAT TO DO: Use the map below to locate Mexico, the
United States, and some important bodies of water.

1. Find Mexico on the map and color it.
2. Find the United States on the map and make it a different
color.
3. Look at the compass rose that tells direction on the map.
Is Mexico north, south, east, or west of the United States?

_____

4. Circle the name of the ocean that is west of Mexico.
5. Find the Gulf of Mexico on the map. Is it north, south, east,

or west of Mexico? _____

Social Studies Objectives: The student uses symbols, finds locations, orients maps to determine direction,
and uses scale to determine distance; The student identifies major landforms and bodies of water on maps and
globes.

SOCIAL STUDIES

Name _____   **Date** _____

LINES AND MOVEMENT

In art, lines can be horizontal, vertical, diagonal, zigzag, or curved. In dance, people can move in lines, too.

horizontal	——	flat, or straight ahead
vertical	|	up and down
diagonal	/	slants
zigzag	⌇	goes back and forth
curved	⁀	bends

WHAT TO DO: Try out these movements and tell what kind of line each one makes.

1. Use your arm to draw a big **S** in the air. What kind of line

did your arm draw? _____

2. Walk straight ahead for five steps. What kind of line did

you walk? _____

3. Stand up. Put your feet together and hold your arms

straight up in the air. What kind of line does your body

make? _____

4. Point one arm straight out in front. Lower it a little. What

kind of line does your arm make? _____

5. Make a big **W** in the air with your arm. What kind of line

did you make? _____

Arts (Dance) Objectives: The student demonstrates movements in straight and curved pathways; The student demonstrates kinesthetic awareness, concentration, and focus in performing movement skills.

THE ARTS

Name_____ **Date**_____

Names of lines describe how they move.

WHAT TO DO: Draw a picture of a place you know with lines.

1. Select the  tool.

2. Draw lines.

vertical

horizontal

diagonal

zigzag

3. Use different kinds of lines to draw a picture of a place you know.

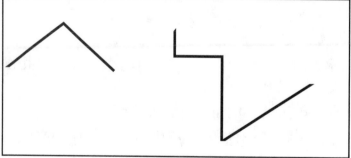

Technology Objective: The student uses software programs with graphics to enhance learning experiences.

TECHNOLOGY

6

Name _____ Date_____

SYNONYMS

In art, different lines are sometimes used to show the same shape. Sometimes two or more words mean the same thing. Words that mean almost the same thing are called *synonyms.*

WHAT TO DO: Look at each sentence below. Find the word in the list that is a synonym for the underlined word and write it after the sentence.

thick   thin   smooth
rough   broken   solid

1. We tried to find <u>gapped</u> lines in Joseph Stella's painting.

_____

2. The middle of the painting has many <u>narrow</u> lines.

_____

3. A <u>wide</u>, diagonal line cuts across the painting.

_____

4. Stella did not use <u>bumpy</u> lines in the artwork.

_____

5. Some of the lines are <u>unbroken</u>.

_____

6. Most of the lines in the painting are straight and <u>even</u>.

_____

Reading/Language Arts Objectives: The student develops vocabulary (word meanings) through reading; The student uses resources to find correct spellings, synonyms, or replacement words.

LANGUAGE ARTS

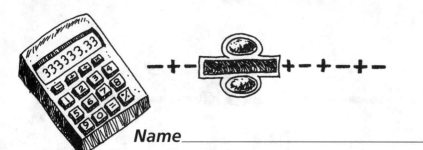

Name_____ Date_____

HOW MANY ON BEAR STREET?

In the painting *The White Way I*, the artist used lines to show what New York City is like. It takes a lot of lines to show how big and busy New York City is.

WHAT TO DO: Figure out the number of things on Bear Street. The first one is done for you. When you finish, count the things on Bear Street to check your answers.

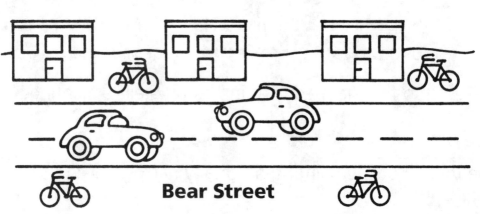

Bear Street

1. There are two cars on Bear Street. Each car has four wheels. To find the number of wheels, add 4 two times.

4 + 4 = __8__   There are _8_ wheels.

2. There are three buildings on Bear Street. Each building has three windows.

3 + 3 + _____ = _____   There are _____ windows.

3. There are four bicycles on Bear Street. How many wheels are there?

_____ + _____ + _____ + _____ = _____

There are _____ wheels.

Mathematics Objectives: The student generates a list of paired numbers based on a real-life situation such as number of tricycles related to number of wheels; The student solves problems using a problem-solving model that incorporates understanding the problem, making a plan, carrying out the plan, and looking back to evaluate the solution.

Name _____ Date _____

LIVING AND NONLIVING THINGS?

The artist Joseph Stella used lines to show his feelings about New York City in his painting *The White Way I*. Besides lines, what other things can be found in a big city like New York?

WHAT TO DO: The pairs of things below can be found in a big city. Decide which is a picture of a living thing and which is a picture of a nonliving thing. Circle each picture of a living thing.

SCIENCE

Science Objective: The student compares and contrasts biological and non-biological objects from the past and present (biological to biological, non-biological to non-biological, and biological to non-biological).

Name _____   Date _____

CITY AND COUNTRY

The painting *The White Way I* shows one artist's feelings about life in a big city. Living in a city is different from living in the country. Here are two words you should know. Read them and the sentences next to them.

urban   The word **urban** describes things about cities and towns.

rural   The word **rural** describes things about the country.

WHAT TO DO: Read the words below. Decide which belong under the word **Urban** and which belong under the word **Rural.** Write each word under either **Urban** or **Rural.**

rancher   skyscraper   crops   forest   taxicabs

hotels   farmer   subway   traffic jams   ranger

Urban   **Rural**

_____   _____

_____   _____

_____   _____

_____   _____

Social Studies Objective: The student distinguishes between urban and rural.

SOCIAL STUDIES

Name _____ Date _____

LINES AND MUSIC

Artists use different kinds of lines to show different shapes, objects, or feelings. In music, groups of sounds can make you feel different ways just as lines do in art. Sounds in music can also make you think of shapes or space, just as lines do in art.

WHAT TO DO: Listen to a favorite song. Draw lines as you listen to the song. Explain your drawing.

+---+
| |
| |
| |
| |
| |
+---+

1. What is your favorite song? _____

2. Now, complete two sentences about your drawing. The sample sentence might help you get started.

Sample sentence: I used <u>broken</u> lines when <u>the</u> <u>music</u> <u>was</u> <u>fast</u>.

_____

_____

_____

_____

Arts (Music) Objective: Identify similarities and differences in the meanings of common terms used in the various arts.

THE ARTS

Name_____ Date_____

Lines can be thick or thin, rough or smooth, or solid or broken.

WHAT TO DO: Draw a picture using many kinds of lines.

1. Select the ⌷ tool.

2. Draw lines.

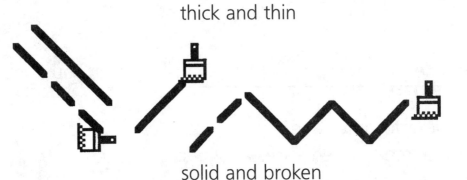

thick and thin

solid and broken

3. Select the ⌷ tool.
Draw rough lines.

4. Draw a picture using all these kinds of lines.

TECHNOLOGY

Technology Objective: The student uses software programs with graphics to enhance learning experiences.

Name_____ Date_____

A PEACEFUL POEM

Horizontal and vertical lines can give a calm feeling to art.
Some words can give the same feeling to writing.

WHAT TO DO: Write a four-line poem about Monet's painting.

1. Begin by thinking of all the words that describe the feelings
Monet's painting shows. Make a word web as shown.

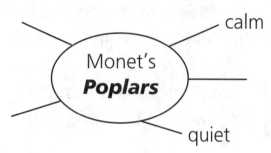

calm

Monet's
Poplars

quiet

2. Write a title for your poem. Then use the words in your web
to write four sentences about the trees. Read the sample
poem for ideas.

Sample poem: Your poem:

My Bedroom

My bedroom is quiet at night.   _____
The blankets are soft and warm.
My kitten purrs at my feet.   _____
I soon fall fast asleep.

_____

_____

_____

Reading/Language Arts Objectives: The student writes to record ideas and reflections; The student
generates ideas for writing by using prewriting techniques (such as drawing, writing key thoughts).

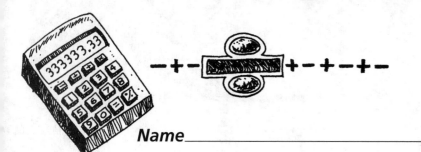

Name_____   Date_____

FRACTIONS

In Monet's *Poplars,* the painting is divided into parts by the lines of the trees and the ground. In math, we use fractions to talk about parts of a whole.

 One half of this circle is shaded. The fraction for one half looks like: $\frac{1}{2}$

 Two thirds of this square is shaded. The fraction for two thirds looks like: $\frac{2}{3}$

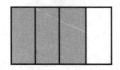 Three fourths of this rectangle is shaded. The fraction for three fourths looks like: $\frac{3}{4}$

WHAT TO DO: Write fractions to tell what part of each shape is shaded. Write the correct fraction on the line next to the shape. The first one is done for you.

 $\frac{1}{4}$ 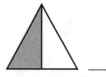 _____   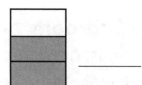 _____

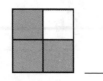 _____    _____   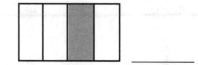 _____

Mathematics Objective: The student uses fraction language (words such as "one third" and "three fourths") to describe a variety of concrete representations of fractional parts of a whole object or set of objects.

Name _____ Date _____

PARTS OF A PLANT

Artists and scientists describe the world in different ways. Claude Monet described a group of trees in his painting *Poplars*. How would a scientist describe a tree?

WHAT TO DO: Look at the tree to learn about the parts of plants. Then, do the activity.

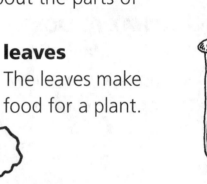

leaves
The leaves make food for a plant.

stems
The stem of a plant is between the root and the leaves. The trunk of a tree is a stem.

roots
The roots of a plant usually grow underground. Plants use their roots to get water from the soil.

Now draw a carrot growing in the soil. Label the following parts of the carrot: leaves, stem, roots.

Science Objective: The second-grade student classifies and sequences objects according to their parts.

Name _____ Date _____

PRODUCTS MADE FROM TREES

Think about trees. In art, we can think about the beauty of trees. In science, we can think about the parts of trees and what they do. In social studies, we can think about how we use trees.

WHAT TO DO: Two products made from trees are paper and wood. Many things are made of paper or wood. Under each picture below, write **paper** or **wood.** The first one is done for you.

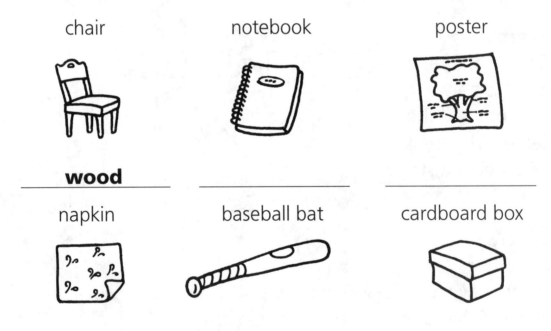

| chair | notebook | poster |

wood _____   _____   _____

| napkin | baseball bat | cardboard box |

_____   _____   _____

Name one thing in your home that is made of wood. _____

Name one thing in your home that is made of paper. _____

Social Studies Objective: The student discusses how one is a consumer of items in the home or school.

SOCIAL STUDIES

Name _____   Date _____

DESIGNING A MOOD

A painting like *Poplars* would make a good stage backdrop for a play about a quiet day in nature. A stage backdrop is a big picture that helps show where a story takes place. It can also help create a feeling or mood for a play.

WHAT TO DO: Create a picture that could be used for a stage backdrop.

1. Think of a story you would like to put on as a play. It could be a fairy tale that takes place among Monet's poplar trees.
Write the name of your story. _____

2. What mood do you want for your play?
Write a word that describes the mood. _____

3. Draw a picture that shows the place the story happens and the mood. Use crayon or colored pencil.

THE ARTS

Arts (Theater) Objective: Visualize environments and construct designs to communicate locale and mood using visual elements (such as space, color, line, shape, texture) and aural aspects using a variety of sound sources.

*Name*_____ *Date*_____

Horizontal and vertical lines are calm.

WHAT TO DO: Draw a calm picture.

1. Select the 🖌 and 🖍 tools.

2. Draw calm lines.

vertical

horizontal

3. Draw a calm picture. Use many horizontal and vertical lines.

Technology Objective: The student uses software programs with graphics to enhance learning experiences.

TECHNOLOGY

Name _____ Date _____

FACT AND OPINION

You can talk about a painting. You can tell what you know about a painting in different ways or what you think. When you tell what you know is true, you are telling a fact. When you tell what you think, you are giving your opinion.

WHAT TO DO: Read the sentences below about the painting *Improvisation with Green Center*. Write an **F** before each sentence that tells a fact. Write an **O** before each sentence that tells an opinion.

_____ **1.** The name of the artist is Wassily Kandinsky.

_____ **2.** *Improvisation with Green Center* is Kandinsky's best painting.

_____ **3.** There are diagonal and swirly lines in the painting.

_____ **4.** There are bright colors in the painting.

_____ **5.** *Improvisation with Green Center* is a pretty painting.

_____ **6.** Wassily Kandinsky was a Russian painter.

_____ **7.** The painting needs more red color in it.

_____ **8.** The painting should be called *Moving Lines and Bright Colors.*

_____ **9.** *Improvisation with Green Center* is not a sculpture.

_____ **10.** Exciting paintings are better than peaceful paintings.

Reading/Language Arts Objective: The student distinguishes fact from opinion in various texts (such as news, advertisements, informational texts).

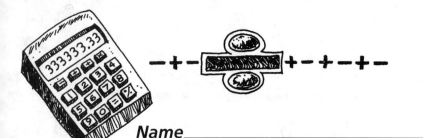

Name_____ Date_____

ESTIMATING TIME

Look at *Improvisation with Green Center*. It gives the feeling that a lot is happening in a short time. Other paintings give the feeling that a little is happening over a long time. Can you tell how much time it takes for something to happen?

WHAT TO DO: Decide whether an activity takes about a second, a minute, or an hour. Read the examples.

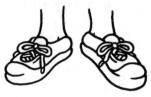

It takes about a **second** for a frog to leap.

It takes about a **minute** to put on and tie your shoes

It takes about an **hour** to do your homework.

Write which activity takes about one second, one minute, or one hour.

1. Washing your face takes about one_____.

2. Walking two miles takes about one_____.

3. Drawing a dot takes about one_____.
Now think of activities you can do that take about a second, a minute, or an hour.

4. It takes about a second to_____.

5. It takes about a minute to_____.

6. It takes about an hour to_____.

Mathematics Objective: The student describes activities that take approximately one second, one minute, and one hour.

Name _____ **Date** _____

USING YOUR SENSES

Wassily Kandinsky's painting is about color, rhythm, and movement. Our sense of sight lets us enjoy artwork. We use all of our senses to learn what is going on around us.

WHAT TO DO: Tell how your senses of smell, touch (or feel), hearing, taste, and sight give you information. What clues would your senses give you? Circle the letter of the right answer.

SCIENCE

Imagine that an empty building nearby has caught fire.
1. What would you smell?
　　a. smoke　　　　**b.** flowers　　　　**c.** soap

2. What would you feel?
　　a. bumps　　　　**b.** cold　　　　**c.** heat

3. What would you hear?
　　a. flames　　　　**b.** a cat　　　　**c.** a doorbell

4. What would you taste?
　　a. marshmallows　**b.** ashes in the air　**c.** burnt toast

5. What would you see?
　　a. dogs and cats　**b.** trucks　　　**c.** flame

Your senses would give you clues that something was wrong. Then you could get help.

Science Objective: The student identifies and researches the importance of living things' sense organs in gathering information about their surroundings.

Name _____   Date _____

PUTTING HISTORY IN ORDER

Wassily Kandinsky was Russian. He lived during an important time in Russian history. Many changes were happening there. Below are sentences about some important times in American history. Which events happened first?

WHAT TO DO: The events below are <u>not</u> in the correct order. On the lines below, number the events in order.

_____ **A.** Bill Clinton became president of the United States.

_____ **B.** The Pilgrims arrived in America on the Mayflower.

_____ **C.** The northern and the southern parts of the United States fought against each other in the Civil War.

_____ **D.** American astronaut Neil Armstrong was the first person to walk on the moon.

_____ **E.** George Washington was the first president of the United States.

Social Studies Objective: The student, on listening to or reading historical stories, myths, and narratives, can place events about the past in correct sequence.

SOCIAL STUDIES

Name _____ Date _____

CREATE A DANCE

Imagine that you are a famous dancer. Create a dance that's like the painting *Improvisation with Green Center*. The painting uses lots of diagonal and curved lines.

WHAT TO DO: Create a dance with a beginning, middle, and end. This list of movements might help you. You can also choose music.

hop	skip	jump	twirl
run	walk	walk backwards	leap
gallop	slide	sit	stand
roll your head	form shapes	rock	zigzag walk

1. Choose movements for each part of your dance.
Beginning movements:

_____, _____, and _____.
Middle movements:

_____, _____, and _____.
End movements:

_____, _____, and _____.

2. Choose three words that describe both your dance and the painting.
My dance and the painting are both _____,

_____, and _____.

Arts (Dance) Objective: Students create a sequence with a beginning, middle, and end, both with and without a rhythmic accompaniment; identify each of these parts of the sequence.

THE ARTS

Name_____ Date_____

Diagonal, zigzag, and curved lines show excitement.

WHAT TO DO: Draw an active picture.

1. Select the ⌷ tool.

2. Draw active lines.

diagonal

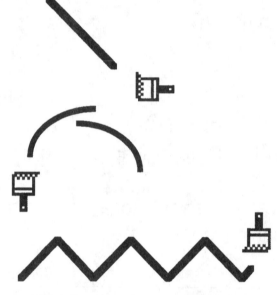

curved

zigzag

3. Draw an active picture using diagonal, curved, and zigzag lines.

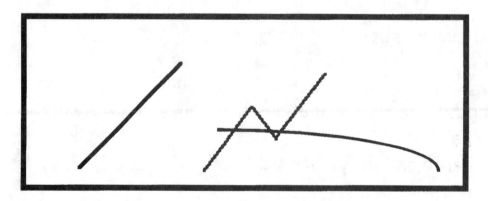

Technology Objective: The student uses software programs with graphics to enhance learning experiences.

TECHNOLOGY

24

Level 2, Unit 1, Lesson 5
ART CONNECTIONS:
Composition on the Word "Vie"

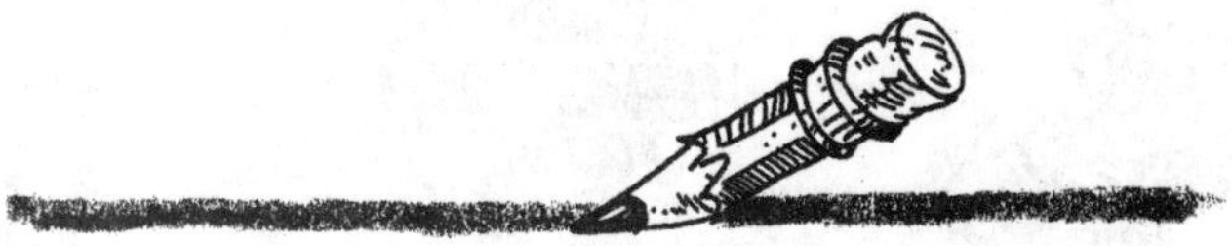

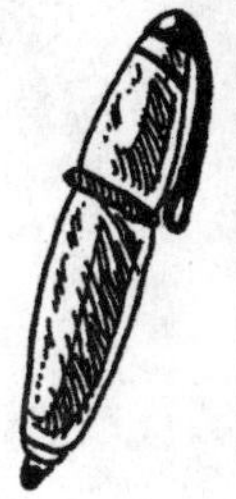

Name ______________________________ **Date** ______________

PLURALS

When you look at the painting, *Composition on the Word "Vie,"* you see more than one circle, triangle, and rectangle. Plurals help us talk about objects when there are more than one.

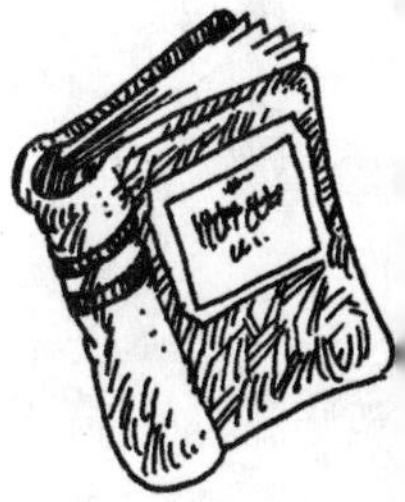

WHAT TO DO: Learn how to form plurals and how to use them.

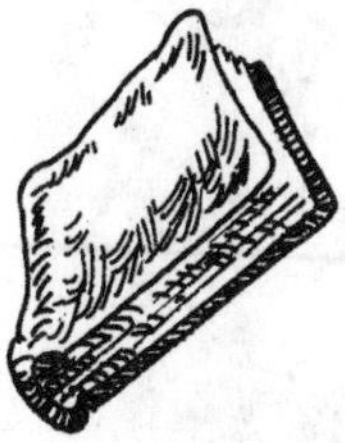

Plurals are often formed by adding an **s** to the word. Write the plural form of each word in the box.

word	plural
circle	***1.***
triangle	***2.***
rectangle	***3.***

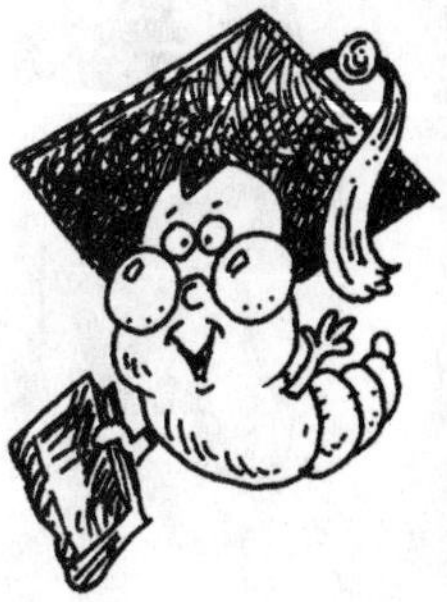

Now, write a sentence for each of the words you wrote.

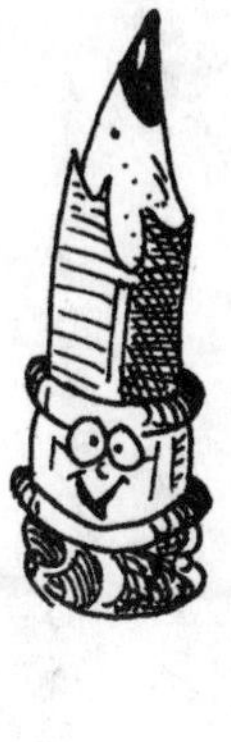

____

____

____

____

Reading/Language Arts Objective: The student uses conventions of grammar and usage (including subject-verb agreement, plurals, verb tenses).

Name_____ Date_____

USING A BAR GRAPH

Many squares, circles, triangles, and rectangles are in the painting. Mr. Johnson's class started looking for these shapes in their classroom. They made a bar graph showing what they found.

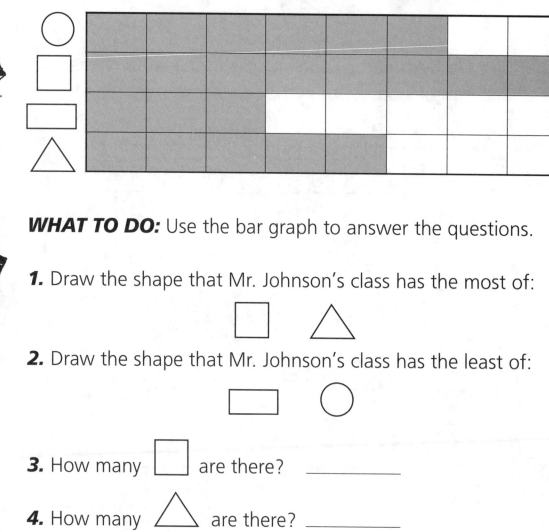

Shapes in Mr. Johnson's Classroom

WHAT TO DO: Use the bar graph to answer the questions.

1. Draw the shape that Mr. Johnson's class has the most of:

2. Draw the shape that Mr. Johnson's class has the least of:

3. How many ⬜ are there? _____

4. How many △ are there? _____

Mathematics Objective: The student draws conclusions and answers questions based on graphed data.

Name _____ Date _____

MAMMALS, BIRDS, AND FISH

Look at the painting. How can you tell which shapes are triangles? You can group shapes by the things they have in common. You can group animals the same way.

WHAT TO DO: One way to sort animals is to decide whether they are mammals, birds, or fish.

mammals   Mammals have hair or fur. They breathe air with their lungs. Mammals are born alive, instead of as eggs.

birds   Birds have feathers, wings, and beaks. They breathe air with their lungs. They lay eggs.

fish   Fish live in water. They have fins and scales. They breathe through their gills.

Decide whether each of the animals below is a mammal, a bird, or a fish. Write your answer below each picture.

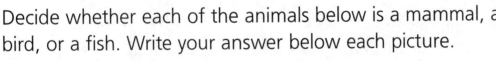

swordfish   **monkey**   **turkey**

_____   _____

Science Objective: The student sorts and analyzes objects according to like properties.

SCIENCE

27

Name _____ Date _____

AT THE SHAPES STORE

Imagine you have stepped into the painting. Now you live in a world of shapes.

WHAT TO DO: You own a store that sells squares. Mark an **X** in front of the answer that makes sense for each question. Talk about your answers with your classmates.

1. You sell squares for 10¢ each. A store opens next door that sells squares for 9¢ each. To sell your squares, you should:

_____ **a.** lower your prices.

_____ **b.** raise your prices.

2. Your squares are better than the other store's squares. You can sell your squares for:

_____ **a.** a higher price than the other store.

_____ **b.** a lower price than the other store.

3. Your store has too many squares! To sell them faster, you should:

_____ **a.** raise your prices.

_____ **b.** lower your prices.

4. There aren't enough to go around, so you can:

_____ **a.** raise your prices.

_____ **b.** lower your prices.

Social Studies Objective: The student describes the purpose of markets, where sellers compete to sell the same or similar products and buyers have choices.

SOCIAL STUDIES

Name _____ **Date** _____

FORMING SHAPES

Imagine you are going to do a dance about different shapes like the ones in the painting. How will you make the shapes?

WHAT TO DO: Find ways to use your body to make shapes in dance. You can also use two or more dancers to make a shape.

1. Tell how you will make a square.

_____

2. Tell how you will make a circle.

_____

3. Tell how you will make a triangle.

_____

Now decide which shapes are formed by the movements.

4. Curve your arms above your head and hold your hands

together. What shape does it make? _____

5. Have three people lie on the floor. Make sure each person's head is next to another person's feet. Make the lines

connect. What shape does it make? _____

THE ARTS

Arts (Dance) Objective: Students explore, discover, and realize multiple solutions to a given movement problem, choose their favorite solution, and discuss the reasons for that choice.

Name_____ Date_____

Squares, circles, triangles, and rectangles are geometric shapes made with lines.

WHAT TO DO: Draw a shape picture with geometric shapes.

1. Select the ▢ shape tool.

Click + and drag.

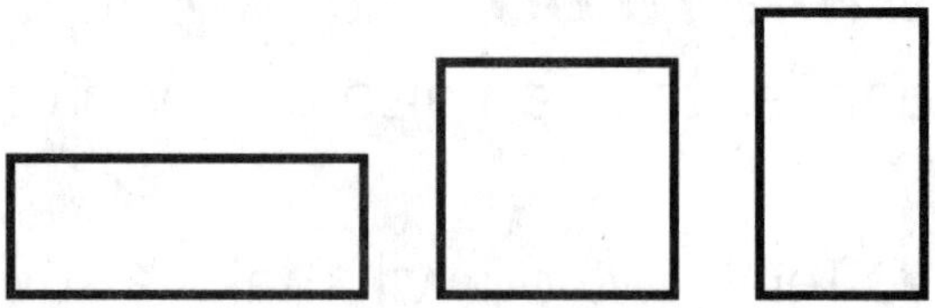

2. Select the ⬭ shape tool.

Click + and drag.

3. Select the ➘ tool.

Draw triangles.

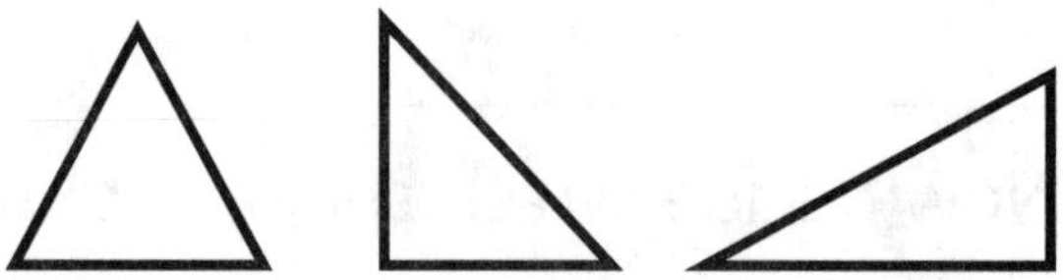

4. Draw a shape picture using different sizes of geometric shapes.

Technology Objective: The student uses software programs with graphics to enhance learning experiences.

TECHNOLOGY

Name_____ Date_____

CAPITALIZATION AND PUNCTUATION

The sentences below are all about shadow puppets from Indonesia. The problem is, they don't follow these rules for capitalization and punctuation:

• The first letter in a sentence should be capitalized.
• Names should be capitalized.
• Every sentence needs punctuation at the end, such as a period.
• Sentences that ask questions should end with question marks.

WHAT TO DO: Read the sentences about *Shadow Puppet.* Below each, write the sentence again using correct capitalization and punctuation.

1. the puppet is from indonesia

_____

2. do you think the puppet has a big nose

_____

3. my friend maya likes the puppet

_____

4. does the puppet have ten toes

_____

5. brad says the puppet is colorful

_____

Reading/Language Arts Objective: The student uses capitalization and punctuation with accuracy (for example, capitalizing names and first letters in sentences; using periods, question marks, exclamation points, apostrophes, commas).

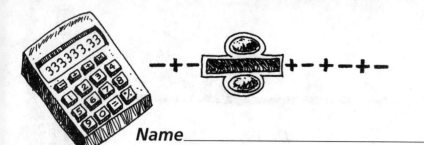

Name_____ Date_____

ADDING COINS

The *Indonesian Shadow Puppet* was made by an artist in Indonesia. Imagine that you are a puppet maker. To make a puppet, you need paper, crayons, glue, and a stick. How much will it cost to buy them?

WHAT TO DO: For each item, add the coins together to see how much it costs. Write your answer after the coins. Check here to see how much each coin is worth. The first problem is done for you.

1.   costs

25¢ + 10¢ + 10¢ + 1¢ = 46¢

2.   costs

_____ + _____ + _____ = _____

3.   costs 

_____ + _____ + _____ + _____ = _____

4.   costs

_____ + _____ + _____ + _____ = _____

Mathematics Objective: The student writes the value of a collection of coins.

MATH

Name _____ Date _____

CHANGING SHADOWS

In the shadow puppet plays of Indonesia, the puppets are behind a white screen. A light behind the puppets makes their shadows show on the screen.

WHAT TO DO: Think about how shadows can change during the day. Mark an **X** on the line in front of the correct answer to each question below.

1. When the sun rises in the east, shadows form on which side?

_____ **a**. north

_____ **b.** west

2. When the sun sets in the west, shadows form on which side of objects?

_____ **a.** west

_____ **b.** east

3. At which time would a shadow be longer?

_____ **a.** eight o'clock in the morning

_____ **b.** one o'clock in the afternoon

4. At which time would a shadow be shorter?

_____ **a.** six o'clock in the evening

_____ **b**. noon

Science Objective: The student predicts changes including those in size, weight, color, position, and movement.

SCIENCE

Name _____ Date _____

ABOUT INDONESIA

The shadow puppet is from Indonesia. In this country shadow puppet plays have stayed about the same for more than 500 years. But many other things are changing there.

WHAT TO DO: Read the list of facts about Indonesia.

- In the past, almost all Indonesians were farmers. Now, many people live in cities.
- In the past, most houses were above the ground on stilts. Now, many houses stand on the ground.
- In the past, Indonesia sold spices to other countries. Now it sells oil and other products.

Decide which sentences tell about Indonesia's past and which tell about the country now. Write **past** or **now** in front of each sentence.

_____ **1.** Most houses were built on stilts.

_____ **2.** Many people live in cities.

_____ **3.** Indonesia sold a lot of spices to other countries.

Social Studies Objective: The student examines changes in individuals, families, and communities over time, such as changes in beliefs, traditions, values, and knowledge.

SOCIAL STUDIES

Name _____ Date _____

STORIES ACROSS CULTURES

In the shadow puppet plays of Indonesia, the smaller puppets usually win against the larger puppets. In many stories from around the world, smaller or weaker characters win against bigger or stronger characters.

WHAT TO DO: Think of a story in which a character wins against a bigger, faster, or stronger character. You can choose a story you have heard before.

1. Tell the name of the story. _____

2. Tell the two main characters in the story.

_____ and _____

3. How is the story like a shadow puppet play?

_____

_____

_____

4. Draw a picture from the story.

THE ARTS

Arts (Theater) Objective: Students identify and compare similar characters and situations in stories and dramas from and about various cultures, illustrate with classroom dramatizations, and discuss how theater reflects life.

35

Name_____ Date_____

Free-form shapes are not geometric.
Free-form shapes make people and objects.

WHAT TO DO: Draw a picture using free-form shapes.

1. Select the tool.

2. Draw free-form shapes.

3. Draw a picture using free-form shapes.

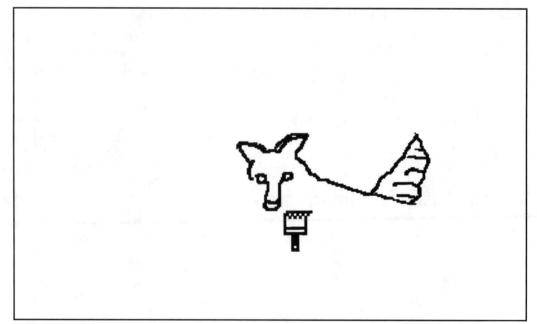

Technology Objective: The student uses software programs with graphics to enhance learning experiences.

TECHNOLOGY

Name_____ Date_____

A SETTING FOR A STORY

The setting of a story is the time and place it happened. A story set at the Pantheon would be very different from a story set in a mall.

WHAT TO DO: Look back at the picture of the Pantheon in Rome. Imagine you are going to write a story that takes place in the Pantheon. What will your story be like? Answer the questions below.

1. How would you describe the Pantheon in your story? _____

_____

_____

_____

2. The Pantheon was built in ancient Rome. Today, many tourists visit it. Will your story take place in ancient Rome _____

or today? _____

3. What kind of story characters might there be in the Pantheon? Ancient Romans? Tourists? Mice who live in _____

the building? _____

_____

_____

4. What happens in your story? Does someone travel _____

through time? _____

_____

_____

Reading/Language Arts Objective: The student discusses the importance of the setting to a story's meaning.

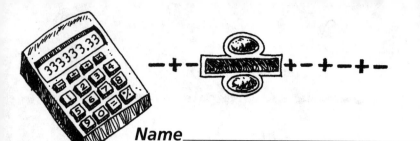

Name_____   Date_____

MATH

ABOUT SOLIDS

Shapes have two dimensions—height and width. Shapes are flat. Sculptures and buildings, though, aren't flat. They have three dimensions—height, width, and depth—and are called forms or solids.

WHAT TO DO: Draw lines to match each item to the form it is most like.

Mathematics Objective: The student uses attributes to describe how two shapes or two solids are alike.

Name _____ Date _____

MEASURING THINGS

When people want to find out the size of something, they measure it. Someone measured the Pantheon in Rome and found out it was about 142 feet tall. To measure something, you need to use units. There are many kinds of units.

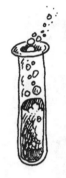

WHAT TO DO: Use paper clips as units to measure the objects below. Then, use an inch ruler and a centimeter ruler to measure the same objects.

Object	Paper Clips	Inches	Centimeters
pencil			
book			
desk			
foot			

Which measuring unit do you think works best? Why?

_____

_____

_____

Science Objective: The student compares and contrasts the accuracy of information gained with and without a variety of standard tools as well as non-standard tools including hands, feet, and classroom material.

Name _____ Date _____

OUR GOVERNMENT AT WORK

The Pantheon was built about two thousand years ago in ancient Rome. At that time, Rome ruled over the cities and countries around it. The Roman government built roads and bridges. It started a postal system for sending letters. It built libraries. What does our government do for you today?

WHAT TO DO: The words shown below name services our government provides for us. Use the best word to complete each sentence.

road   post office   library   school

1. A _____ is a place you can go to mail a letter.

2. People go to _____ to learn things.

3. If you want to borrow a book, you go to a

_____ .

4. People need a _____ to get from one place to another.

5. Which of these services do you think is most important?

Why? _____

_____

Social Studies Objective: The student identifies some government services in the community such as libraries, schools, highways, parks, and postal services, and identifies their value to the community.

SOCIAL STUDIES

Name _____ Date _____

A PLAY ABOUT ROME

Pretend that your class is going to put on a play about ancient Rome. What should you know about ancient Rome before you put on the play?

Here are some facts about ancient Rome.
• Rome was built on seven hills.
• About a million people lived there.
• The ancient Romans fought many wars.
• The people of ancient Rome wore togas. A toga was made from a large sheet of material that was wrapped around the body.
• The ancient Romans watched chariot races. Chariots are two-wheeled carts pulled by horses.

WHAT TO DO: Use the facts about ancient Rome to answer questions about your play. Circle the best answer.

1. Your play could be about
   a. a war.   **b.** a chariot race.   **c.** both.

2. Your actors should wear
   a. togas.   **b.** sneakers.   **c.** funny hats.

3. Your stage should show a
   a. forest.   **b.** lake.   **c.** city.

THE ARTS

Arts (Theater) Objective: Students communicate information to peers about people, events, time, and place related to classroom dramatizations.

Name_____ Date_____

Geometric shapes have matching geometric forms. Shapes are two-dimensional and have height and width. Forms are three-dimensional and have height, width, and depth.

WHAT TO DO: Create a picture of a building using geometric shapes.

1. Select the ▭ and ⬭ shape tools and the ⬎ tool. Draw the outline of a building.

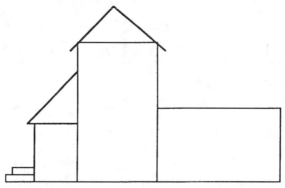

2. Add doors and windows with geometric shapes.

3. Select the ⬎ tool. Add depth with lines.

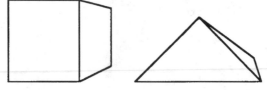

4. Use the 🖌 tool to add patterns to different parts of the building.

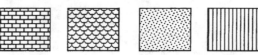

Technology Objective: The student uses software programs with graphics to enhance learning experiences.

TECHNOLOGY

Name_____ Date_____

MANY KINDS OF WRITING

When you write about the mask in the picture *Haida—Portrait Mask,* you need to know why you are writing. Do you want to give information? Do you want to thank someone for a gift?

WHAT TO DO: Write about the mask in several ways.

1. Imagine that a friend who has never seen the mask wants to know about it. Make a list of the mask's features.

_____

_____

_____

2. Pretend that the mask is a gift for you. Finish the thank-you note below. Use the list of features to help you describe what you like about the mask.

Dear_____ ,

Thank you for the mask. I like it because _____

_____

_____

Sincerely,

_____

Reading/Language Arts Objective: The student writes in different forms for different purposes (for example, lists to record, letters to invite or thank, stories or poems to entertain).

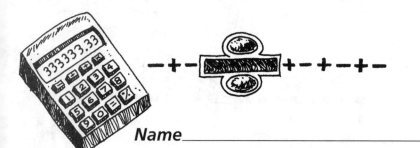

Name_____   Date_____

WHICH IS MORE LIKELY?

More likely means something happens more often than something else. **Less likely** means something happens less often than something else.

WHAT TO DO: Quiana likes to paint masks. The graph shows how many masks were red, pink, yellow, and orange. Use the graph to answer the questions below. Circle the best answer to each item.

Colors of Quiana's Masks

red
pink
yellow
orange

0   1   2   3   4   5   6   7   8

1. A mask is **more likely** to be: pink   yellow

2. A mask is **less likely** to be: orange   red

3. A mask is **more likely** to be: red   pink

4. A mask is **less likely** to be: yellow   orange

5. A mask is **more likely** to be: red   yellow

Mathematics Objective: The student uses data to describe events as more likely or less likely.

Name _____ **Date** _____

RECYCLING

The mask in the picture is made from string, wood, and other materials. Art is sometimes made from materials that have been used before. Other items can be made from recycled materials too.

WHAT TO DO: Think of ways to use the recyclable materials below. Explain your new use for the item in the second column.

Item	Tell About It
milk carton	
newspaper	
plastic cut	
glass jar	

Science Objective: The student creates uses for recyclable materials.

Name _____ Date _____

PROTECTING THE ENVIRONMENT

The mask in the picture is made from different materials, including wood. Wood has been used to make art for thousands of years. Wood is also used to make many other things, like furniture, paper, houses, and boats. How can we protect the trees that give us wood?

WHAT TO DO: Circle the pictures below that show ways to help protect trees. Put an **X** through the pictures that show ways trees can be harmed. Then, complete the sentence to tell what you can do to help protect trees.

I can protect trees by _____

_____

Social Studies Objective: The student identifies actions that can protect the environment (for example, recycling, conserving, and replenishing).

SOCIAL STUDIES

Name _____ Date _____

MUSIC EVERY DAY

Masks are used for many reasons. They are used in celebrations. They are used in plays or dances. Music is also used for many reasons.

WHAT TO DO: Decide which kind of music is best for each event below. Then tell why you chose that kind of music.

quiet	loud	fast	slow
funny	serious	exciting	soothing

Event	Kind of Music	Why?
1. You are trying to put a baby to bed.		
2. You are putting on a silly puppet play.		
3. A dentist wants her patients to feel calm.		
4. You are leading an exercise class.		

THE ARTS

Arts (Music) Objective: Students identify various uses of music in their daily experiences and describe characteristics that make certain music suitable for each use.

47

Name_____ **Date**_____

The shape of the face is a free-form shape.

WHAT TO DO: Create a mask that shows a feeling.

1. Select the ⬭ shape tool, the ✏ tool, or the 🖌 tool. Draw a face shape.

2. Add eyes, a nose, a mouth, and eyebrows to show a feeling.

3. Finish the mask by adding more details.

4. Use the 🖌 tool to add color to match the mood.

TECHNOLOGY

Technology Objective: The student uses software programs with graphics to enhance learning experiences.

Name _____ **Date** _____

ABOUT THE SCULPTURE

Artists often tell a story in their work. Sometimes it is hard to figure out what story the artist is telling. Take another look at the sculpture, *The Emergence of the Clowns.* What do you think is happening in the sculpture?

WHAT TO DO: Study the sculpture. Decide what you think is happening. Then, decide what you think the clowns will do next.

1. The clowns look like they're climbing up out of something.

What do you think they're climbing out of? _____

_____

2. Look at the faces of the clowns. How do you think they

are feeling? _____

3. What do clowns usually do? _____

_____

Now finish the story the artist started. Write at least two complete sentences.

4. _____

_____

_____

Reading/Language Arts Objectives: The student writes to develop and refine ideas; The student composes complete sentences in written texts.

Name_____ Date_____

MATH

ESTIMATING LENGTH

How did the artist who made *The Emergence of the Clowns* know what size the arms, fingers, and other parts of the clowns should be? Often we can tell **about** how long something should be, even if we don't know **exactly** how long it is.

WHAT TO DO: Estimate the length of the items below.

Circle the items that in real life are about an **inch** long. Mark an **X** on the items that in real life are about a **foot** long.

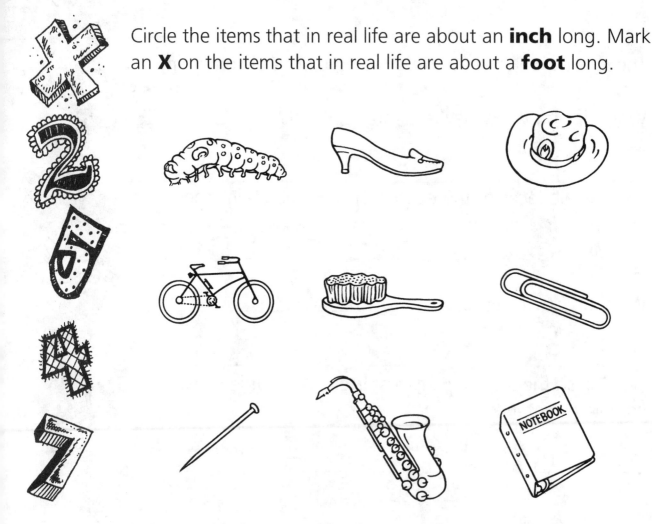

Mathematics Objective: The student identifies concrete models that approximate standard units of length, capacity, and weight.

Name _____   Date _____

PRODUCTS OF THE EARTH

The clowns in the sculpture, *The Emergence of the Clowns,* are made from clay. Clay comes from the earth. Right now, people aren't worried that we will run out of clay. But we need to be careful with other products of Earth, such as water.

WHAT TO DO: Match the ways we use water with the ways we can try to help save water.

Take shorter showers.

Water the lawn less often.

Keep litter out of lakes, streams, and rivers.

On the back of this paper, write a sentence about how to help save water.

Science Objective: The student designs ways to conserve materials that come from the earth.

Name _____ Date _____

THE STATE OF NEW MEXICO

Roxanne Swentzell, the artist who made *The Emergence of the Clowns,* is a Pueblo Indian. Many Pueblo Indians live in New Mexico. The map below will tell you a little about the state of New Mexico.

WHAT TO DO: Use the map to finish the sentences below. Look at the key to tell what the symbols mean, and use the compass rose for directions.

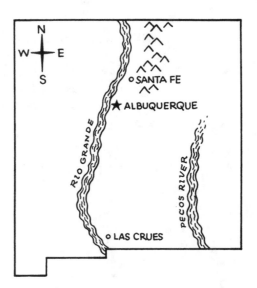

Circle the correct answer.

1. The **Pecos River   Rio Grande**   flows through New Mexico from north to south.

2. Santa Fe   Albuquerque   is the capital of New Mexico.

3. The city of Santa Fe is in the   **mountains   flat land**.

4. The Pecos River is   **east   west**   of the Rio Grande.

5. Santa Fe is   **north   south**   of Las Cruces.

Social Studies Objective: The student interprets and uses symbols on a map.

Level 2, Unit 2, Lesson 3
ART CONNECTIONS:
The Emergence of the Clowns

Name _____ Date _____

DESCRIBING MOVEMENT

The clowns in the sculpture, *The Emergence of the Clowns,* almost seem to be moving. In dance, there are many different ways to talk about movement.

WHAT TO DO: Imagine that the clowns in the sculpture are dancing. Look at the picture carefully. Then, tell how the clowns appear to be moving.

1. Which way do the clowns look like they are moving?

  up   down

2. At what speed do the clowns seem to be moving?

  fast   slow

3. Which direction do the clowns look like they are moving?

  forward   backward

4. The words below describe actions. Underline the five words that best tell what one or more of the clowns is doing.

  climbing   hopping   running   laying
  spinning   stretching   sleeping   jumping
  leaning   sneezing   diving   looking

THE ARTS

5. Write a name for the dance the clowns are doing. Tell why

the name fits the dance. _____

_____

Arts (Dance) Objective: Students attentively observe and accurately describe the action (such as skip, gallop) and movement elements (such as levels, directions) in a brief movement study.

Name_____ Date_____

People are free-form three-dimensional forms. Bodies have height, width, and depth.

WHAT TO DO: Create a picture of yourself as a clown in action.

1. Select the ✏ tool or the 🖌 tool. Draw an outline of your body in action.

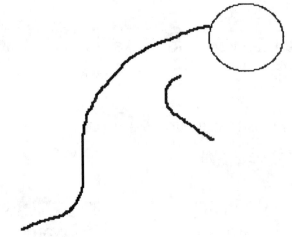

2. Add details to show depth.

3. Use the 🖌 tool to add color to your body.

Technology Objective: The student uses software programs with graphics to enhance learning experiences.

TECHNOLOGY

54

Name _____ **Date** _____

THE PARTS OF A BOOK

In the painting *Jungle Tales,* children are listening to an adult read a book about the jungle. How can you tell what a book is going to be about? How do you know whether you want to read it? You can learn a lot about a book by looking at its cover and title page.

WHAT TO DO: Use the book cover and title page to answer these questions.

1. Write the title of the book. _____

2. Who wrote the book? _____

3. Who illustrated the book? _____

4. Think about the book's title and the picture. Finish this

sentence. I think this book is about _____

_____

Reading/Language Arts Objective: The student recognizes that different parts of a book offer information (such as cover, title page, author, illustrator).

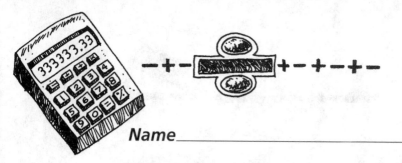

Name_____ Date_____

READING A THERMOMETER

The woman in the painting *Jungle Tales* is reading a book about the jungle. The temperature in a jungle usually stays between 70°F (Fahrenheit) and 90°F. You can tell temperature by reading a thermometer like the ones shown here.

WHAT TO DO: Read the thermometers, and write the temperatures in the blanks. Then, answer the questions.

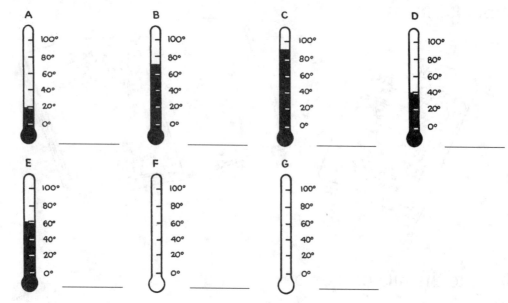

1. What is the lowest temperature shown?_____

2. What is the highest temperature shown?_____

3. Which thermometer shows a temperature at which you

might swim outside? _____

4. Which temperature is good for polar bears?_____

5. Show 30° on thermometer F.

6. Show 80° on thermometer G.

Mathematics Objective: The student reads a thermometer to gather data.

Name _____ Date _____

ANIMALS AND PLANTS

The children in the painting *Jungle Tales* are listening to stories about the jungle. The jungle is known for its many animals and plants. How can you tell if something is a plant or an animal?

WHAT TO DO: Write **Plants** or **Animals** before each of the statements below.

_____ **1.** usually stay in the same place

_____ **2.** usually lay eggs or give birth to live young

_____ **3.** can usually move around on their own

_____ **4.** grow leaves, fruits, nuts, or flowers

_____ **5.** grow hair, scales, fur, or feathers

_____ **6.** usually grow seeds to reproduce

_____ **7.** usually make their own food from sunlight and air

_____ **8.** eat food instead of make their own food

9. Circle the words that name a part of a plant.
Underline the words that name a part of an animal.

stem	lung	roots	gills	stomach
legs	leaf	flower	fur	feather

Science Objective: The student observes differences in the structures and functions of plants and animals.

Name _____   Date _____

MAKING DECISIONS

In the painting *Jungle Tales,* a mother decided to read a story to her children. For every decision we make, there are possible outcomes. Outcomes are things that happen because of something we do.

Decision	Possible Outcomes
Read the children a story.	• The children will need help understanding parts of the story. • The children will like the story and want to read on their own.

WHAT TO DO: Write two possible outcomes for each decision.

Decision	Possible Outcomes
Drop your clothes on the floor.	1. 2.
Put clothes in a hamper.	1. 2.
Do your homework.	1. 2.

Social Studies Objective: The student charts choices and possible outcomes as an aid to making responsible decisions.

SOCIAL STUDIES

Name _____ **Date** _____

CREATING A STORY DANCE

The children in *Jungle Tales* seem to like the book the mother is reading. What is your favorite book or story? What do you like about it?

WHAT TO DO: Make a dance based on your favorite book or story. The dance can tell the story, or it can have the same feeling as the story. Use the questions below to help you create your dance.

1. What is the name of your book or story? _____

_____

2. What is the story about? _____

_____

_____

3. Name any characters from your story you want to have in your dance.

4. Which of the following words best describe the feeling you want for your dance? Circle them.

joyful	exciting	scary	happy	sad
angry	silly	serious	nervous	thoughtful

5. On another sheet of paper, draw a picture showing the characters that you would use in your dance. Be sure to show costumes and feeling.

Arts (Dance) Objective: Students improvise, create, and perform dances based on their own ideas and concepts from other sources.

THE ARTS

Name_____ Date_____

Artists overlap shapes to show depth.

WHAT TO DO: Create an overlapping picture of people playing.

1. Select the 🖌 tool or the ✒ tool. Draw outlines of people playing.

2. Show depth by moving your shapes so they overlap. Use the ✎ tool to select each shape. Drag each shape to a position that overlaps another shape.

3. Use the 🖌 tool or the ✒ tool to add a background.
4. Use the 🪣 tool to add color to your picture.

Technology Objective: The student uses software programs with graphics to enhance learning experiences.

TECHNOLOGY

Name_____ Date_____

PAINTING A PICTURE WITH WORDS

Pretend you are going to describe the apples in *Still Life with Apples* for a friend who has never seen the painting. What words would you use?

WHAT TO DO: Write a sentence that paints a picture of the apples with words.

Start with this sentence to tell about the apples:
There are apples in the painting.

1. Add a word or words to the sentence that tells how many apples. Write the word or words in the blank.

There are _____ apples in the painting.

2. Tell how many apples there are. Then, use a word to tell

how large the apples are. There are _____,

_____ apples in the painting.

3. Now add a word or words to describe the color of the apples. In the first blank, tell how many apples there are. In the second blank, tell what size they are. In the third

blank, tell what color they are. There are_____,

_____, _____ apples in the painting.

4. Read all your sentences again. Which one paints a better picture with words? Why?

Reading/Language Arts Objective: The student revises selected drafts for varied purposes (including to achieve a sense of audience, precise word choices, and strong images).

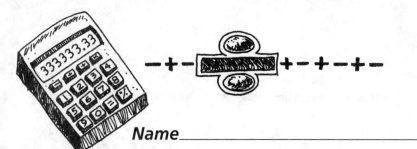

Name_____   Date_____

MATH

COUNTING APPLES

When the artist painted *Still Life with Apples,* he painted one of the most popular fruits in the world. How can you tell how many apples there are? Start by counting the apples on this page.

WHAT TO DO: Counting is easier if you can group things by ten. Do the problems below.

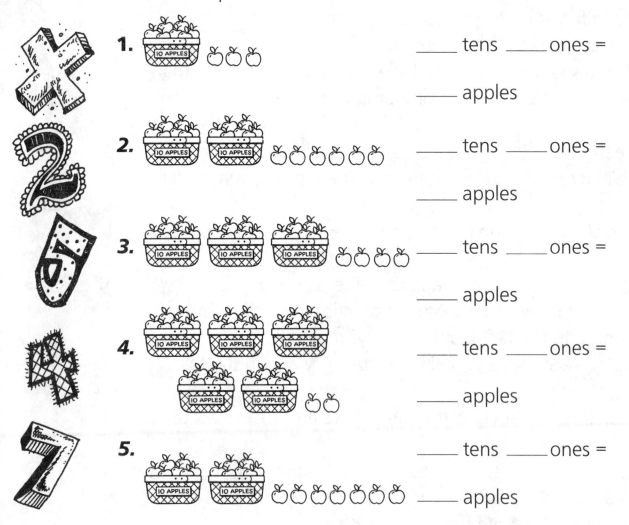

1. _____ tens _____ ones =

_____ apples

2. _____ tens _____ ones =

_____ apples

3. _____ tens _____ ones =

_____ apples

4. _____ tens _____ ones =

_____ apples

5. _____ tens _____ ones =

_____ apples

Mathematics Objective: The student uses concrete models of hundreds, tens, and ones to represent, compare, and order whole numbers

Name _____   Date _____

THE NEEDS OF LIVING THINGS

The painting *Still Life with Apples* shows a table covered with apples. Apples come from trees, which are living things. Living things, such as animals and plants, need certain things to stay alive and healthy.

WHAT TO DO: The picture shows some of the important needs of living things. Read the paragraphs below and fill in the blanks.

1. The _____ gives us warmth and light. Most plants

need the _____ to make food with their leaves.

Animals need the _____ to stay warm.

2. Even though we can't see it, _____ is very

important to living things. Animals breathe _____

through their lungs. Plants use _____ and sunlight to make food with their leaves. Even animals and plants that

live in the ocean get _____ from the water around them.

3. Most animals drink _____. Most plants use their

roots to get _____ from the soil. All living things

need _____.

Science Objective: The second-grade student describes the needs of living things.

Name _____ Date _____

GOING SHOPPING

An artist's job is to make art. In *Still Life with Apples,* the artist painted apples. Pretend your job is to pick apples. What would you do with the money you earn?

WHAT TO DO: Pretend you have earned a total of $100 picking apples. Now you're going to the store. Study the items below carefully. Circle the items you will buy with $100. Add the items carefully to make sure they total $100 or less.

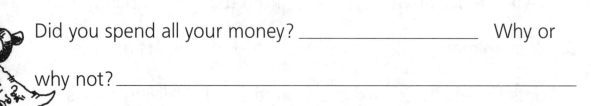

radio $40	video player (VCR) $100	movie tickets $10	television $80
athletic shoes $65	jeans $25	CD $15	jacket $30
bicycle $90	camera $50	athletic shoes $65	book bag $30

Did you spend all your money? _____ Why or

why not?_____

Social Studies Objective: The student participates in an activity that simulates the opportunity to earn and spend money.

SOCIAL STUDIES

Name _____   Date _____

PEOPLE IN MOTION

A still-life painting, like *Still Life with Apples,* shows things that do not move. People are not like still life. They are almost always in motion.

WHAT TO DO: Think about some of the ways people move. Then, decide how dance is different from other kinds of movement.

Ways People Move

play sports	ride a bike	mix or stir things	smile	point
walk	hug	ride in a wheelchair	jog	build things

In some ways, dance is different from other kinds of movement. Write **yes** or **no** in front of each sentence about dance.

_____ **1.** A dance can tell a story.

_____ **2.** Dance steps or movements are often planned ahead of time.

_____ **3.** Dance is always slow.

_____ **4.** Dance can create a mood or feeling.

_____ **5.** A dance never includes running or hopping.

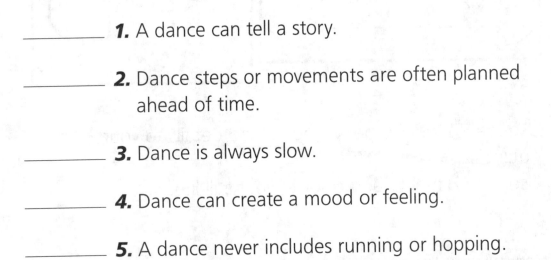

Arts (Dance) Objective: Students observe and discuss how dance is different from other forms of human movement (such as sports, everyday gestures).

THE ARTS

Name_____ Date_____

Artists draw or paint overlapping objects in a still life to show depth.

WHAT TO DO: Create a still life showing depth.

1. Collect interesting objects for a still-life drawing. Place them together on a desk or table.

2. Draw a still life of the outline of the objects. Overlap the shapes to show depth. Use a variety of tools:

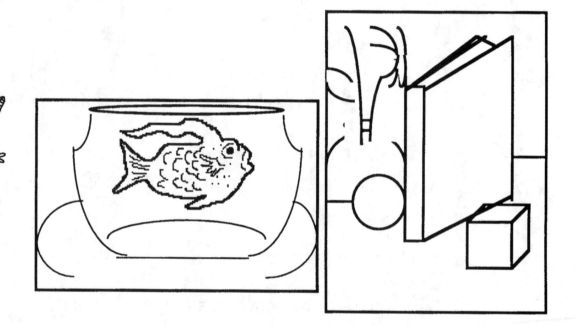

3. Use the 🖌 tool or the ✏ tool to add details to your outlines.

4. Use the 🪣 tool to add color to your still life.

Technology Objective: The student uses software programs with graphics to enhance learning experiences.

66

TECHNOLOGY

Name_____   Date_____

THE MAIN IDEA

The sculpture *Votive Horse* was made in India, a country on the continent of Asia.

WHAT TO DO: Read the paragraph. Then decide what the paragraph is about and what details it tells you about India.

India

Around one billion people live in India. It is the second largest country in the world in population. The only country in the world that has more people than India is China. In fact, about one out of every six people in the world lives in India.

1. Put an **X** next to the sentence that best tells the main idea of the paragraph. If you're not sure, read the paragraph again. What does it talk about the most?

_____ **a.** India has a lot of horses.

_____ **b.** India is in Asia.

_____ **c.** A lot of people live in India.

_____ **d.** More people live in China than in any other country in the world.

2. In the paragraph, underline the sentences that support the main idea you marked above.

Reading/Language Arts Objective: The student recognizes main ideas and supporting details in informational text, and themes in stories and poems.

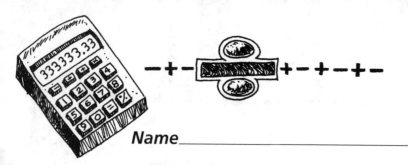

Name_____ Date_____

MAKING A GRAPH

Artists can show what animals look like. They show the height, width, and depth of animals. You can use a graph to show how many animals there are.

WHAT TO DO: Complete the bar graph to show how many animals there are at the West Town Zoo.

The West Town Zoo

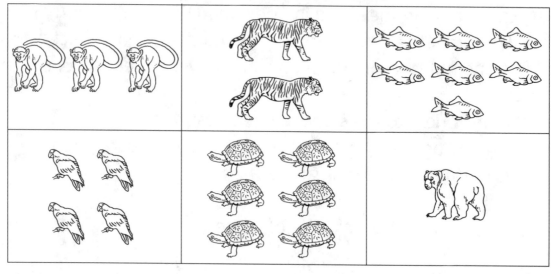

Animals at the West Town Zoo

	0	1	2	3	4	5	6	7	8
monkeys									
tigers									
goldfish									
parrots									
turtles									
bears									

Mathematics Objective: The student constructs picture graphs or bar-type graphs.

Name _____ Date _____

WATCHING ANIMALS

Artists watch real animals carefully before they put them in their art. Scientists watch animals carefully, too. They look at what an animal does and how its body works.

WHAT TO DO: Three science students wrote observations of animals. Can you figure out what kind of animal each student was watching?

Kiesha: I saw a long, thin animal that had no arms and no legs. It wriggled back and forth on the ground. Its skin was smooth and shiny and made of scales. It had a small head, and it stuck out its tongue a lot. The tongue was long and thin and forked at the end.

1. What animal did Kiesha see? _____

Jason: The animal I saw had fluffy fur, long ears, long back legs, and a short, fluffy tail. It hopped when it moved. Its nose moved a lot.

2. What animal did Jason see? _____

Beth: I saw an animal with a round shell. Only its head, feet, and tail stuck out of the shell. It could swim in the water and walk on the ground. When it got scared, it pulled its feet, head, and tail into its shell.

3. What animal did Beth see? _____

Science Objective: The student compares and contrasts his or her own observations with those of others.

SCIENCE

Name_____ Date_____

DIFFERENT WAYS TO LEARN

Votive Horse was made in India a long time ago. You can find out more about things that happened in history by looking in different places. You might look in a dictionary, an encyclopedia, or a book at a library.

WHAT TO DO: Imagine you want to know more about the American space program during the 1960s. Match each way to learn with the kind of information you might find. Draw a line between each matching pair.

Way to Learn

1. Look up spacecraft in a **dictionary.**

2. Look up space exploration in an **encyclopedia.**

3. Read a **book** about astronauts landing on the moon.

Kind of Information

a. You will read memories of what the space program was like during the 1960s.

b. You will find a few pages telling about space exploration and the history of the American space program.

c. You will find a few sentences telling what a spacecraft is.

Social Studies Objective: The student names several sources of information about a given period or event.

SOCIAL STUDIES

Name _____   Date _____

GETTING THE IDEA ACROSS

The sculpture *Votive Horse* doesn't look like a real horse. It looks enough like a horse, though, so that you get the idea of a horse. How can you get the idea of a horse across in theater, even if you don't have a real horse? Costumes and props can be used to get the idea across.

WHAT TO DO: Imagine you are putting on a play about a horse. Design a horse costume. Think about the materials, such as paper, cloth, paint, and string, you might use to make the costume. Draw a picture of your horse costume here.

1. How would the actor playing the horse behave?

2. Tell about a prop you could use to give the idea of a horse.

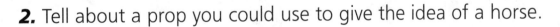

Arts (Theater) Objective: The student compares how ideas and emotions are expressed in theater, dramatic media, dance, music, and visual arts.

THE ARTS

Name_____ Date_____

Animals are three-dimensional forms. They have height, width, and depth.

WHAT TO DO: Create a scene with an animal in it.

1. Draw an animal in motion. Position the body parts to show depth. Use a variety of tools: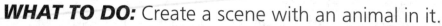

2. Add a background. Overlap lines and shapes.

3. Use the ✍ tool to add color to your picture.

Technology Objective: The student uses software programs with graphics to enhance learning experiences.

TECHNOLOGY

Name_____ Date_____

FACT AND FANTASY

Creatures like the half-person and half-bird in *Baird Trogon* aren't real. They are fantasy. Many stories and books have creatures in them that are fantasy, too. Books can also tell us about real animals. How can you tell the difference between fact and fantasy?

WHAT TO DO: Write **fact** or **fantasy** in the blank to tell whether each of the sentences is fact or fantasy.

_____ **1.** A whale lives in the ocean.

_____ **2.** Cinderella's pumpkin changed into a coach.

_____ **3.** The girl grew wings and flew away.

_____ **4.** There are fifty states in the United States.

_____ **5.** The eggs in the story could talk.

_____ **6.** Trees have roots, stems, and leaves.

_____ **7.** Birds have beaks and feathers, and they lay eggs.

_____ **8.** The creature in the painting *Baird Trogon* talks to you.

_____ **9.** An elephant told me a funny joke about a monkey and a snake.

_____ **10.** The cow jumped over the moon.

Reading/Language Arts Objective: The student distinguishes fantasy from fact.

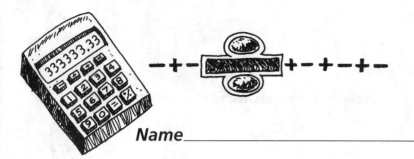

Name_____ Date_____

COMPARING SHAPES

The artist who painted *Baird Trogon* painted a creature that is half-person, half-bird. Birds and people are very different from each other. Shapes can be alike in some ways and different in others.

WHAT TO DO: Tell how each pair of shapes is alike and how it is different.

1.

_____

_____

2.

_____

_____

3.

_____

_____

Mathematics Objective: The student uses attributes to describe how two shapes or two solids are different.

Name _____ **Date** _____

SEEING COLORS

Light is made up of colors. An object gets its color from the color of the light it reflects. For example, a stop sign looks red because it reflects the red part of light.

WHAT TO DO: Write what color of light each object reflects.

Science Objective: The student evaluates the earth's resources, including the sun.

SCIENCE

Name _____ Date _____

PROTECTING BIRDS

The artist who painted *Baird Trogon*, Robert Lostutter, is very interested in the study of birds. Many kinds of birds are in trouble because of the way people have treated the environment. Today, people are finding new ways to help save birds by using technology.

WHAT TO DO: Read the facts below. Then, give your ideas.

• Sometimes there are only a few birds of a certain kind left. People use technology to help eggs hatch in a safe place.
• People who count birds out in the woods may use the satellites to track where the birds live.
• Computers help people know when and where it is safe to cut down trees.

Write a paragraph telling how you would use technology to help protect birds.

_____

_____

_____

_____

Social Studies Objective: The student suggests technological advances that have helped protect the environment.

SOCIAL STUDIES

Name _____ **Date** _____

BIRD DANCE

Look at the painting *Baird Trogon*. How would you create a dance about a creature that was half-person, half-bird?

WHAT TO DO: Create a dance about a half-person, half-bird. Design a costume for your dance. Draw a dancer wearing the costume.

Now, make up movements or choose movements from the list that show how a bird moves.

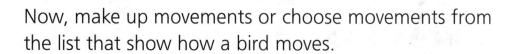

run, jump, skip, hop, flap arms, squat, twirl, kick, stretch, gallop, slide, point, clap, walk, bend your knees, bob your head

1. Tell the movements you would use to show a bird flying.

_____

2. Tell the movements you would use to show a bird walking.

_____

THE ARTS

Arts (Dance) Objective: The student creates a dance project that reveals understanding of a concept or idea from another discipline (such as pattern in dance and science).

Name_____ Date_____

Artists use primary and secondary hues, or colors, in their artwork.

WHAT TO DO: Create a design filled with primary and secondary colors.

1. Select the 🖌 tool. Draw your favorite shape.

2. Draw your shape three more times. Place part of each new shape on top of the one you drew before, so it overlaps.

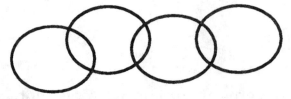

3. Use the 🖢 tool to add the primary colors to the shapes. Begin with yellow. Then, add red and blue and then, yellow again.

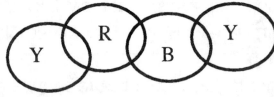

4. Fill the overlapped spaces with secondary hues. Use the color that would be created by mixing the two primary colors on each side of the overlapped space.

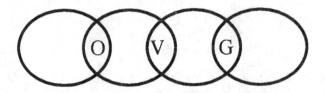

Technology Objective: The student uses software programs with graphics to enhance learning experiences.

78

TECHNOLOGY

Name _____ Date_____

WRITING ABOUT A TOPIC

The photograph of the Flat Iron Building was taken in 1905. If you visit New York City today, you can still see the Flat Iron Building.

WHAT TO DO: Read the paragraph about a trip to New York City. Underline the sentences that do not have anything to do with the trip to New York.

Last summer my family took a trip to New York City. While we were there we visited Central Park. I don't like strawberry ice cream. The next day we visited the Statue of Liberty. Yesterday my cat had kittens. The last thing we did was to visit the top of the Empire State Building. My house is small. My whole family had fun during our trip. My cousin lives in Florida.

Reading/Language Arts Objective: The student responds constructively to others' writing.

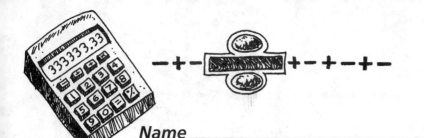

Name_____   Date_____

MATH

ADDITION

The Flat Iron Building is just one of the many buildings in New York City. You can use addition to count things like buildings.

WHAT TO DO: Use addition to find out how many objects are in each row. Write the addition problem you used.

1. How many buildings?

2. How many fish?

3. How many trees?

Mathematics Objective: The student models, creates, and describes problem situations in which equivalent sets of concrete objects are joined or formed.

Name _____ Date _____

PREDICTING CHANGES

In art, the word **value** means lightness or darkness. As the light changes, colors look different.

WHAT TO DO: The colors of things look different to us, depending on how much light is shining on them. Decide how colors change when there is less light or more light.

1. Circle the source of light that makes colors look most light.

SCIENCE

2. Circle the source of light that makes colors look most dark.

3. Draw a beach scene as it would look in the middle of a sunny day.

4. Draw a beach scene as it would look at night.

Science Objective: The student predicts changes including those in size, weight, color, position, and movement.

Name _____ *Date* _____

PHOTOGRAPHS

The photograph of the Flat Iron Building shows what New York City was like in 1905. What kinds of things can you tell about the past by looking at old photographs?

WHAT TO DO: Imagine you wanted to learn about New York City in 1905. After each question below, write whether you would best learn the answer from old **photographs** or from words in a **book**.

• What did the clothing look like in 1905? _____

• What did the cars look like in 1905? _____
• How many people were living in New York City

  in 1905? _____

• Who was the mayor of the city back then? _____
• What did the buildings in New York City look like

  back then? _____

• In 1905, did all children go to school? _____

Social Studies Objective: The student uses evidence such as photographs and interviews to compare various interpretations of the same time period.

SOCIAL STUDIES

Name _____ Date _____

PITCH

In art, the word *value* tells how light or dark something is. In music, the word *pitch* tells how high or low a sound is.

WHAT TO DO: Decide which musical instruments have high or low pitch. Here's a clue: most small instruments have high pitch, and most large instruments have low pitch.

Circle the one that has the **higher** pitch.

1. violin   cello

2. tuba   trumpet

Circle the one that has the **lower** pitch.

3. snare drum   bass drum

4. bassoon   flute

THE ARTS

Arts (Music) Objective: The student identifies the sounds of a variety of instruments, including many orchestra and band instruments, and instruments from various cultures, as well as children's voices and male and female adult voices.

Name_____ Date_____

Value is the lightness or darkness of a color.

WHAT TO DO: Create a design filled with grays—values of black and white.

1. Select the ◿ or ⬠ or ▢ shape tool and draw a shape.

2. Use the same shape tool to draw three or four more shapes around the first shape.

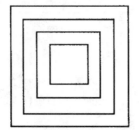
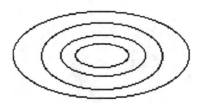

3. Select the 🖌 tool and a light gray color. Fill the second shape with the gray.

4. Use the 🖌 tool to add a darker gray to each of the next shapes.

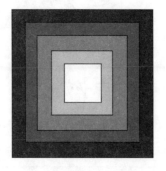
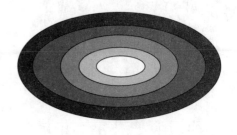

Technology Objective: The student uses software programs with graphics to enhance learning experiences.

TECHNOLOGY

Name _____ **Date** _____

SEASONS

The painting *Solstice* shows the first day of winter. What does the painting tell you about winter?

WHAT TO DO: Read about the four seasons. On another piece of paper, draw a picture to show each season.

The Four Seasons

The four seasons are spring, summer, winter, and fall. Many plants grow flowers in the spring, and many animals have babies. In summer, the weather gets hotter. Days are longer. People wear lighter clothing. Fall is also called autumn. Autumn is the time when many crops are ready to be picked. Apples and pumpkins are harvested in autumn. In winter, the weather gets colder. The days get shorter. People wear heavier clothing.

Reading/Language Arts Objective: The student reads (or listens) and responds to informational text in various ways (including use of illustrations, displays, demonstrations, available technology).

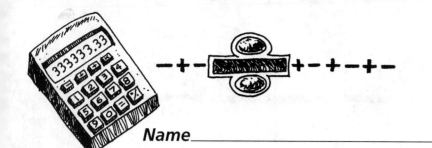

Name_____ Date_____

PATTERNS

The painting *Solstice* shows the first day of winter. Seasons always follow the same pattern: spring, summer, fall, winter. In math, you can look at patterns to tell what comes next too.

WHAT TO DO: Look at the pattern. Fill in the missing numbers.

1. 1	2		4		6	
2. 2		6	8	10		
3. 5	10		20			
4. 3		9	12			
5. 15			30			
6. 8	10			16		
7. 5	6		8			
8. 10	20	30				
9. 8		12	14			
10. 11	12				16	

Mathematics Objective: The student finds patterns in numbers.

Name _____   Date _____

PATTERNS AND SEASONS

The painting *Solstice* shows the first day of winter. In some places, the weather changes a lot during the year. In other places, the weather doesn't change as much.

WHAT TO DO: Label each picture as spring, summer, fall, or winter. Then, number the pictures **1** through **4** to show the correct order. Start with spring as number **1**.

season: _____   number: _____   season: _____   number: _____

season: _____   number: _____   season: _____   number: _____

Science Objective: The student identifies, predicts, and compares events and objects that appear in patterns.

Name _____ Date _____

WEATHER AND SEASONS

The painting *Solstice* shows a wintry scene. In some places, people do things in the winter that they can't do at any other time of the year.

WHAT TO DO: Make a list of items for each season where you live. Tell about the weather and the activities you do during each season.

Spring   **Summer**

_____   _____

_____   _____

_____   _____

_____   _____

Fall   **Winter**

_____   _____

_____   _____

_____   _____

_____   _____

Social Studies Objective: The student describes weather patterns, seasonal patterns, and natural hazards.

88

Name _____ Date _____

DIALOGUE

Look at the painting *Solstice*. Imagine there is a boat in the water. Imagine two people in the boat are talking to each other. What would they say? In a play, what they say is called **dialogue.**

WHAT TO DO: Create a dialogue between two people floating in a boat on the water in the painting.

Write your characters' names here:

_____ and _____

Choose a topic for your characters to talk about. Write

your topic here: _____

Write what your characters say to each other. For each number, write the character's name in the first blank. Write what he or she says in the second blank.

1.	First Character:	
	Second Character:	
2.	First Character:	
	Second Character:	

THE ARTS

Arts (Theater) Objective: The student improvises dialogue to tell stories, and formalizes improvisations by writing or recording the dialogue.

Name_____ Date_____

Artists use light values, or tints, in their artwork to create misty, foggy scenes. Tints are created by adding white to a color.

WHAT TO DO: Create an outdoor scene using only tints, or light values, of colors.

1. Select the ⬛ tool and the ◿ ⬭ ⬜ shape tools. Draw an outdoor scene that shows a mood. Draw with light values of colors - pink, light blue, light green, light violet, and so on. Show a time of day and season.

2. Use the ⬛ tool and the 🖌 tool to fill areas or objects with color.

Technology Objective: The student uses software programs with graphics to enhance learning experiences.

TECHNOLOGY

90

Name _____ Date _____

WRITING CLEAR MESSAGES

What do you think *Spectator of the Sea* is trying to show?
Sometimes artists do not want their art to have a clear
meaning. When you write a message, it should be easy to
understand.

WHAT TO DO: Ryan wrote a phone message for his brother
Ted. Rewrite Ryan's message so that it makes more sense.

What happened:
The phone rang and Ryan answered it. His brother Ted's friend,
Jerry, was calling. Ted wasn't home, so Ryan took a message
for him. Jerry wanted Ted to play baseball tomorrow at
1 o'clock. Jerry said Ted could call him back until 7 o'clock
tonight.

Dear Ted,
Your frend Jerry cald. You can't play baseball with him
yesterday at 1 o'clock. Jerry sed you can't call him bak until
7 o'clock tonight.

_____

_____

_____

_____

_____

Reading/Language Arts Objective: The student writes messages that can be read by others (for example,
by spelling conventionally familiar and regular words).

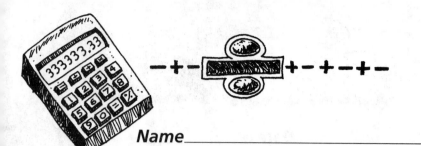

Name_____ Date_____

MATH SYMBOLS

In the painting *Spectator of the Sea*, the artist used symbols from different cultures. A symbol is something that stands for something else. Do you know what the math symbols below stand for?

WHAT TO DO: Write the symbols for less than (**<**), greater than (**>**), and equal to (**=**) to compare the numbers.

1. 20 _____ 10   **6.** 33 _____ 25

2. 55 _____ 55   **7.** 84 _____ 97

3. 90 _____ 90   **8.** 7 _____ 8

4. 12 _____ 13   **9.** 35 _____ 28

5. 61 _____ 67   **10.** 43 _____ 34

Mathematics Objective: The student uses numbers and symbols to record quantities and their comparisons.

Name _____ Date _____

SEA PLANTS AND ANIMALS

The word *spectator* in the title of the painting means "someone who watches something." What would you really see if you watched sea creatures?

WHAT TO DO: Read about animals of the sea. Then, answer the questions.

Sea Animals

Sea animals come in many shapes and sizes. Some have smooth bodies and swim. Some have legs and crawl on the ocean bottom. Some sea animals look like plants, but they eat bits of food that float by instead of making food from sunlight.

1. What size are sea animals?

_____

2. What do some sea animals look like?

_____

3. Do sea animals with legs usually live at the top or

bottom of the ocean? _____
4. How do these animals move?

_____

_____

Science Objective: The student observes differences in the structures and functions of plants and animals.

SCIENCE

Name _____ Date _____

A SYMBOL OF OUR COUNTRY

In the painting *Spectator of the Sea*, the artist used symbols from different cultures. A symbol stands for something. Do you know some symbols used by the United States?

WHAT TO DO: Draw the United States flag. Then, answer the questions.

SOCIAL STUDIES

1. What three colors are used in the flag?_____ ,

_____ , and _____ .

2. The stripes in the flag stand for the first states. How many

states were there? _____

3. Each of the stars stands for one of the states that make up the United States. How many states are there in the United

States? _____

Social Studies Objective: The student illustrates the flags of Texas and the United States and explains what their symbols represent.

Name _____ Date _____

MUSIC SYMBOLS

In the painting *Spectator of the Sea*, the artist used symbols from different cultures. A symbol is something that stands for something else. There are many kinds of symbols used in music.

WHAT TO DO: Notes are one kind of music symbol. Read about musical notes. Then, read the music and tell how many beats each note gets.

Music symbols:

whole note
usually gets four counts

half note
usually gets two counts

quarter note
usually gets one count

eighth note
usually gets half a count

Arts (Music) Objective: The student reads whole, half, dotted half, quarter, and eighth notes and rests in 2/4, 3/4, and 4/4 meter signatures.

THE ARTS

Name_____ Date_____

Artists use dark values, or shades, in their artwork to create dark, moody scenes. Shades are created by adding black to a color.

WHAT TO DO: Create a dark, moody outdoor scene using only shades, or dark values, of colors.

1. Select the 🖌 tool and the ⬗ ⬭ ▭ shape tools. Draw an outdoor scene that shows a mood. Draw with dark values of colors - navy blue, dark green, dark red, and so on. Show a time of day and season.

2. Use the 🖌 tool and the 🪣 tool to add color to areas or objects.

Technology Objective: The student uses software programs with graphics to enhance learning experiences.

TECHNOLOGY

96

Name _____ **Date** _____

GIVING DIRECTIONS

If you could talk to the people in the painting *Gathering Wild Rice*, they could tell you exactly how to pick wild rice. Think of something you know how to do. How would you explain it to someone else?

WHAT TO DO: Write step-by-step directions for something you know how to do.

I know how to _____.

Here are the directions.

Step 1: First, _____

_____

Step 2: Next, _____

_____

Step 3: Then, _____

_____

Step 4: Then, _____

_____

Read your directions to a partner. Ask your partner to tell you whether the directions are clear.

Reading/Language Arts Objective: The student gives directions clearly.

97

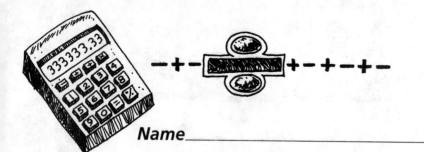

Name_____ Date_____

HOW MUCH IS A POUND?

The people in the painting *Gathering Wild Rice* are gathering rice. You usually buy rice in a store. Rice is sold by weight. Sometimes it is sold by the pound.

WHAT TO DO: Do you know how heavy a pound is? Look at the pictures. They show you about how much some common things weigh. Then, make three lists of items that weigh about as much as a pair of scissors, a pound of rice, and two large books.

2 ounces

1 pound

2 pounds

Less than a pound	About a pound	More than a pound
_____	_____	_____
_____	_____	_____
_____	_____	_____
_____	_____	_____
_____	_____	_____
_____	_____	_____

Mathematics Objective: The student uses concrete models that approximate standard units to measure length, capacity, or weight.

Name _____ Date _____

FOOD CHAINS

The painting *Gathering Wild Rice* shows people gathering food. All living things need food. All living things are part of a food chain. All food chains start with the sun. The sun sends out energy that plants use to make their food. Smaller animals then eat the plants. Next, larger animals eat the smaller animals, and so on.

WHAT TO DO: Read about food chains. Then, put each food chain in the right order.

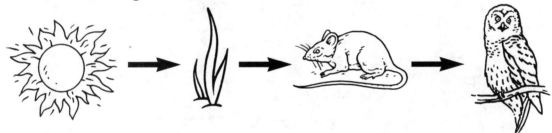

Put each food chain in the right order.
1. chickens, sun, corn, people

The _____ sends energy that _____ makes

into food. _____ eat the corn, then _____
eat chicken.

2. mountain lions, deer, grass, sun

The _____ sends energy that _____ makes

into food. _____ eat the grass, then _____
eat the deer.

Science Objective: The student models the interdependence of living things to each other, including relationships in food chains and food webs.

Name _____ Date _____

GROWING AND GATHERING

The painting *Gathering Wild Rice* shows people getting food to eat. Thousands of years ago, before people learned to farm, all food was gathered or hunted. People ate what they could find in the world around them. Now most of the food we eat is grown on farms.

WHAT TO DO: Look at the nature scene below. Write about the things you see that people could use for food.

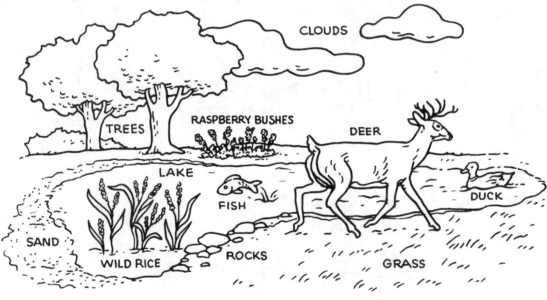

Social Studies Objective: The student describes different ways people satisfy their needs and wants, past and present.

Name _____ **Date** _____

DANCES

The painting *Gathering Wild Rice* was made by a Chippewa artist. His painting shows people doing a traditional activity—gathering wild rice. Music and dance are also traditional activities of the Chippewa.

WHAT TO DO: Read about some dances. Then, answer the questions.

Many dances were done to honor plants and animals that provided food for people. A corn dance for a good harvest was done by the Cherokee. The Plains Indians danced to honor the buffalo, which they hunted for food. The Pueblo did rain-making dances. The Sioux thanked the sun with a sun dance. Sometimes these dances lasted two or three days, and many people would join the dance.

Circle the correct answer:

1. Many dances were done to honor:

    a. plants   **b.** plants and animals   **c.** animals

2. The Plains Indians honored this animal in dances:

    a. dinosaur   **b.** whale   **c.** buffalo

3. In the dry Southwest, the Pueblo danced for:

    a. dust   **b.** rain-making   **c.** thunder

THE ARTS

Arts (Dance) Objective: The student accurately answers questions about dance in a particular culture and time period (for example, In colonial America, why and in what settings did people dance? What did the dances look like?).

Name_____ Date_____

Artists use warm hues, or colors, such as yellow, orange, and red, and cool hues, such as blue, green, and violet, in their artwork.

WHAT TO DO: Create a name design filled with warm colors or cool colors.

1. Select the ⬡ shape tool. Draw a large circle.

2. Select the ➘ tool. Draw the stick letters of your first name inside the circle. Use the ✏ tool to make round letters. Connect the letters and touch the edges of the circle. Turn the letters different ways.

3. Use the 🖑 tool to add either warm or cool colors to all the spaces.

Technology Objective: The student uses software programs with graphics to enhance learning experiences.

TECHNOLOGY

102

Name _____ Date _____

CHARTING INFORMATION

The painting *Spring Ice* shows a scene of early spring in Canada, when the ice on lakes and rivers is melting.

WHAT TO DO: Write facts that you already know about rivers and lakes to complete the chart. You may want to use a science book or encyclopedia for additional information to add to your chart.

Facts About Lakes	Facts About Rivers
1._____ _____	1._____ _____
2._____ _____	2._____ _____
3._____ _____	3._____ _____

Reading/Language Arts Objective: The student records own knowledge base (for example, by listing, webbing, drawing).

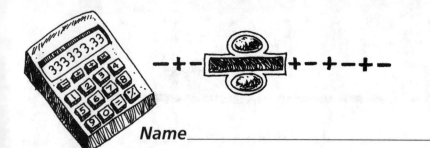

Name_____ Date_____

TELLING TIME

The title of the painting *Spring Ice* tells what time of year it is. We use the seasons to measure long amounts of time. We use a clock to measure short amounts of time.

WHAT TO DO: Can you tell what time it is? Look at the clocks below and write what time it is on each. Use the clock facts listed here to help you.

Write the time for each:

1.

_____ o'clock

2.

_____ o'clock

3.

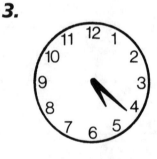

_____ o'clock

4.

_____ o'clock

5.

_____ o'clock

6.

_____ o'clock

Mathematics Objective: The student uses hours and minutes to describe the time shown on a clock.

Name _____ Date _____

FORCE AND MOVEMENT

The trees in the painting *Spring Ice* look calm and still. What would happen to them if the wind started blowing? Wind is a force that makes things move. A **force** is something that pushes or pulls on an object.

WHAT TO DO: Circle the object in each pair that needs a stronger force to move it.

1.

2.

3.

4.

SCIENCE

Science Objective: The student uses wind, water, and swings to describe change in an object's position and the force required for the change.

Name _____ Date _____

LABELING A MAP

The artist who painted *Spring Ice* lived in Canada. Can you find Canada and other places on a map?

WHAT TO DO: Write the labels on the map where they belong.

Map of North America

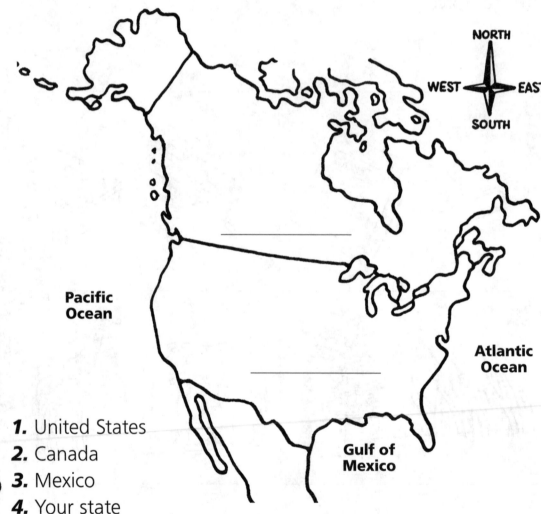

1. United States
2. Canada
3. Mexico
4. Your state

Social Studies Objective: The student locates one's community, Texas, the United States, and selected nations on maps and globes.

Name_____ **Date**_____

A SONG FOR SPRING

The painting *Spring Ice* shows a cold spring day. Imagine you are going to write a song to go with the painting. What kinds of sounds remind you of a cold spring day?

WHAT TO DO: Complete the chart below to tell how you would make sounds to go with different parts of the painting *Spring Ice*.

Part of the Painting	Sound You Would Make
the bare tree branches	
the cracking and melting ice	
the flowing water	
the drifting clouds	

THE ARTS

Now, put the sounds together in a short song about the painting. Share your song with the class.

Arts (Music) Objective: The student improvises short songs and instrumental pieces, using a variety of sound sources, including traditional sounds, nontraditional sounds available in the classroom, body sounds, and sounds produced by electronic means.

Name_____ Date_____

Artists use cool colors to create a cool mood or a frosty, cold scene. Blue, green, and violet are cool colors.

WHAT TO DO: Create a landscape scene using only cool colors.

1. Think of a cold, frosty winter day. Select the 🖌 tool and cool colors. Draw land forms, such as hills, mountains, cliffs, or snow banks.

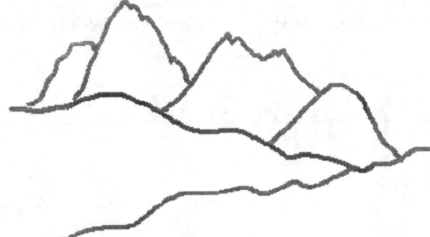

2. Add water forms, such as streams, rivers, puddles, ponds, lakes, or an ocean.

3. Use the 🖌 tool or the ◁ ⬭ ☐ shape tools and cool colors to add trees, plants, animals, people, or objects to your frosty scene.

4. Ask classmates whether they can identify the season and the scene in your picture.

Technology Objective: The student uses software programs with graphics to enhance learning experiences.

TECHNOLOGY

108

Name _____ Date_____

PAINT IT WITH WORDS

You can see paintings with your eyes. Words help paint pictures you can see in your mind. Exact words can make an exciting picture.

WHAT TO DO: The following sentences paint a dull picture of *I Got a Girl on Sourwood Mountain*. Try to paint a more interesting picture by changing the underlined words. Rewrite each sentence.

1. The lamp is <u>moving</u>. The light keeps <u>changing</u>.

_____

_____

2. The musician <u>plays</u> the violin and <u>hits</u> his foot on the floor.

_____

_____

3. The dancers <u>move</u> to the <u>fast</u> rhythm.

_____

_____

Reading/Language Arts Objectives: The student revises selected drafts for varied purposes (including to achieve a sense of audience, precise word choices, and strong images). The student uses conventions of grammar and usage (including subject-verb agreement, plurals, verb tenses).

Name_____   Date_____

MATH

ADDING AGAIN AND AGAIN

A window has parts called panes. In Thomas Hart Benton's painting, there is a window with eight panes.

WHAT TO DO: Read the directions. Draw each window.

1. Draw four windows. Put two panes in each window. On each blank below, write the number of panes in each window. Then, add the numbers. How many panes all together?

_____ + _____ + _____ + _____ = _____

2. Draw three windows. Put four panes in each window. On each blank, write the number of panes in each window. Then, add the numbers. How many panes all together?

_____ + _____ + _____ = _____

Mathematics Objectives: The student models, creates, and describes problem situations in which equivalent sets of concrete objects are joined or formed.

Name _____ Date _____

MUSIC OF ALL KINDS

If you were with the people in the painting, you would hear loud music and other sounds. Sound is created when something *vibrates*, or moves back and forth very fast. You can make music with everyday things. You can rub, hit, or pluck all kinds of objects to make them vibrate.

WHAT TO DO: Look at the objects below. Choose five objects and tell how you could use them to make sound.

SCIENCE

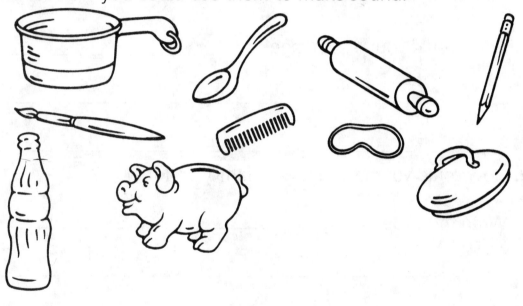

1. _____

2. _____

3. _____

4. _____

5. _____

Science Objective: The student, using various instruments, compares the sounds of vibrating objects, and changes rates of vibrations for comparison.

Name_____ **Date**_____

THINGS TO DO FOR FUN

In *I Got a Girl on Sourwood Mountain*, people are enjoying music and dancing.

Music and dancing were common ways people had fun before TVs, radios, movies, computers, cars, and electric lights.

WHAT TO DO: Imagine that you do not have a TV, radio, computer, car, or electric lights.

1. How would your life change?_____

_____

_____

2. How could you have fun with family and friends?

Write three ideas._____

_____

_____

3. Sometimes it is hard to find things that everyone will like to do. Which of your three ideas do you think the most people

would enjoy?_____

_____

Social Studies Objective: The student identifies alternative solutions to a problem and evaluates the effectiveness of the solution.

SOCIAL STUDIES

Name _____ **Date** _____

WHEN TO CLAP

In *I Got a Girl on Sourwood Mountain*, a man is playing a fiddle. People are dancing to the music and clapping. We don't always dance or clap to music, though. At some performances, people are expected to listen quietly.

WHAT TO DO: Is it all right to clap with the music? In each blank, write **yes** if it is all right to clap along with the music; write **no** if it is not proper to clap along with the music.

_____ **1.** An orchestra is playing in a concert hall.

_____ **2.** The marching band is playing at a school pep rally.

_____ **3.** Someone is singing the national anthem at a football game.

_____ **4.** Music is playing in a movie at a theater.

_____ **5.** Scouts are singing songs around a camp fire.

_____ **6.** A woman is singing at a college graduation.

_____ **7.** A band is playing at a fair.

_____ **8.** A person is playing piano on the stage in front of an audience.

THE ARTS

Arts (Music) Objectives: The student demonstrates audience behavior appropriate to the context and style of music performed.

113

Name ______________________ **Date** ______________

Artists use diagonal and zigzag lines to move your eyes through an artwork and to create visual movement.

WHAT TO DO: Create a design that shows movement with zigzag and diagonal lines.

1. Select the ▭ shape tool. Draw a large box.

2. Select the ⟍ tool. Divide the box into four sections.

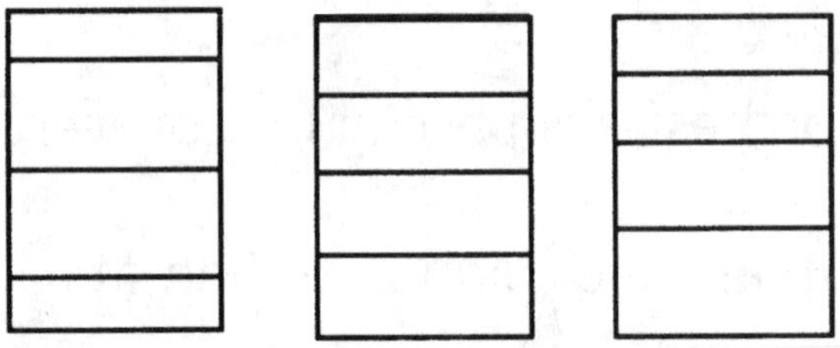

3. Add diagonal or zigzag lines to each section. Use thick and thin lines. Fill each section. ⟍⟍ //

Technology Objective: The student uses software programs with graphics to enhance learning experiences.

LANGUAGE ARTS

Name_____   Date_____

USING CLUES TO READ

The Starry Night shows movement. Curved lines lead your eyes around the painting. When you read, your eyes move across the words. You can use reading clues to understand hard words.

WHAT TO DO: Read the sentences. Use the clues to figure out each underlined word.

See the dark <u>vale</u> between the hills.
Clue 1: a thing you can look at and see
Clue 2: a thing that can be dark
Clue 3: a thing that can fit between hills

1. Now circle the meaning of *vale*.
thought   star   valley

A moon <u>illuminates</u> the night sky.
Clue 1: The word tells something the moon does.
Clue 2: The moon's action changes the sky.
Clue 3: This happens when the sky is dark.

2. Now circle the meaning of *illuminates*.
opens   brightens   closes

Reading/Language Arts Objective: The student uses semantic (meaning), syntactic (word order), and struc-
tural (roots, prefixes, and suffixes) cues in conjunction with phonological knowledge to read.

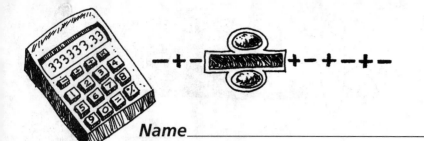

Name_____ Date_____

PROBABILITY

The artist of *The Starry Night* seems to have frozen one bright night in time. In the real world, time doesn't stop.

Sometimes you can tell whether something is likely to happen in the future. You can be pretty sure that the sun will come up tomorrow. You probably can't predict what you'll get for your birthday when you're 27.

WHAT TO DO: Read each sentence below. If you are pretty sure it will happen, write **yes** in the blank. If you can't be sure, write **no**.

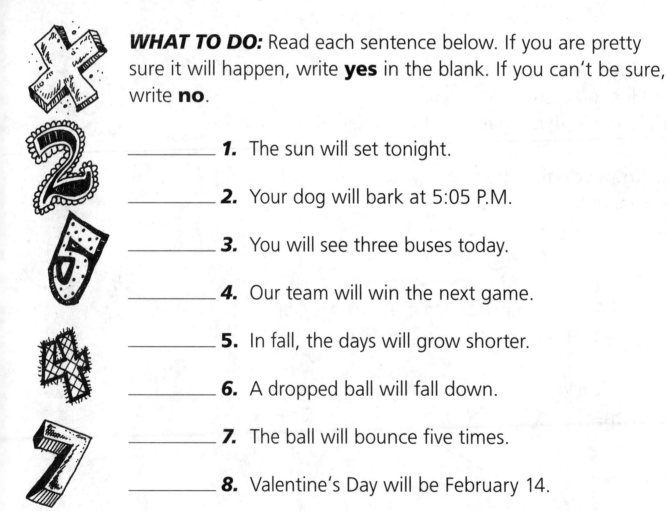

_____ **1.** The sun will set tonight.

_____ **2.** Your dog will bark at 5:05 P.M.

_____ **3.** You will see three buses today.

_____ **4.** Our team will win the next game.

_____ **5.** In fall, the days will grow shorter.

_____ **6.** A dropped ball will fall down.

_____ **7.** The ball will bounce five times.

_____ **8.** Valentine's Day will be February 14.

Mathematics Objective: The student uses data to describe events as more likely or less likely.

116

Name _____   Date _____

IS IT A LIVING THING?

Look at the painting *The Starry Night*. The artist painted both living and nonliving things.

WHAT TO DO: Complete each activity.

1. Name three living things that are shown in the painting.

_____

_____

2. Name three nonliving things that are shown in the painting.

_____

_____

3. Pretend you came from outer space to visit the place in the painting. How would you know that people were there?

_____

_____

4. If a visitor from outer space came to your classroom at night, how would it know people used the room?

_____

_____

Science Objective: The student compares and contrasts biological and nonbiological objects from the past and present.

117

Name _____ Date _____

LIGHTING UP THE DARKNESS

In *The Starry Night*, there are bright stars in the sky and lights in the houses. Before the early 1900s, people didn't have electric lights. Electric lights changed people's lives. New developments or inventions often change the way we live.

WHAT TO DO: Look at the chart. Tell how each invention changed people's lives in each of the areas shown.

Invention	Home	Work
electric lights		
television		
cellular phone		

Social Studies Objective: The student identifies and describes examples in which science and technology have changed the lives of people, such as in homemaking, child care, work, transportation, and communication.

SOCIAL STUDIES

Level 2, Unit 4, Lesson 2
ART CONNECTIONS:
The Starry Night

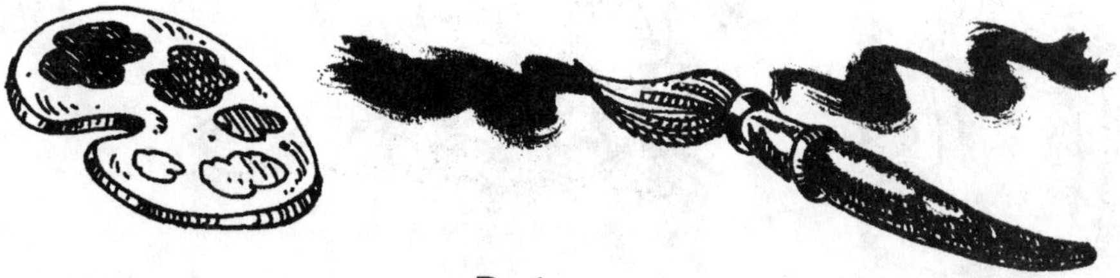

Name ______________________ **Date** ____________

A DANCE THAT SHOWS MOVEMENT AND LIGHT

Do you see swirls of movement when you look at *The Starry Night?* Do you see twinkling lights?

WHAT TO DO: Think of ways that you could show movement and light in a dance. Then, answer each question below.

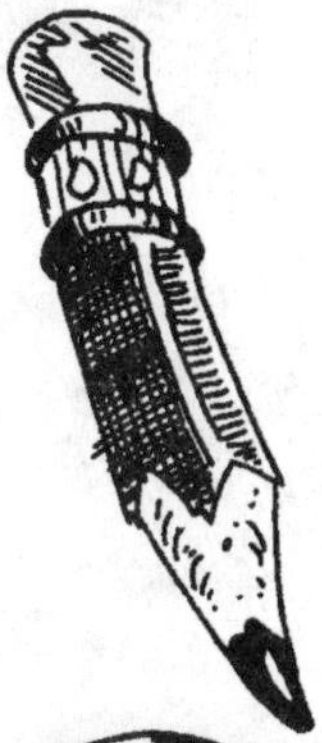

1. How can you show swirls of movement?

____

____

____

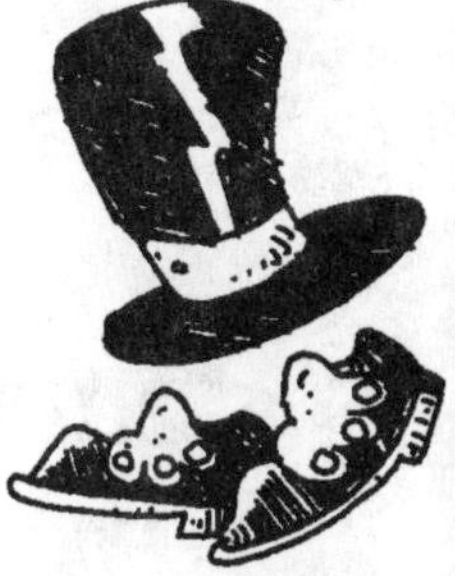

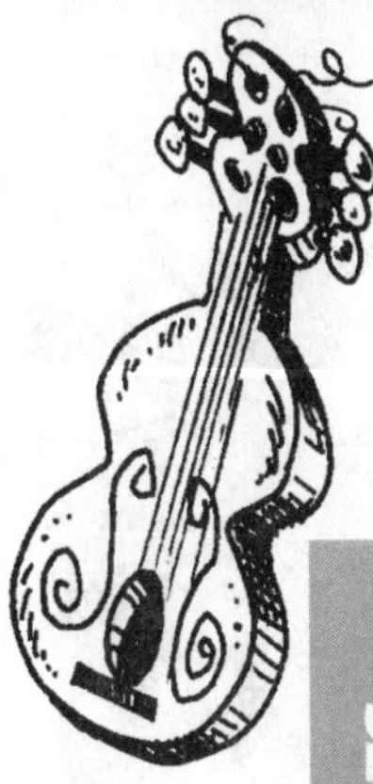

2. How will you show a twinkling, starry sky?

____

____

____

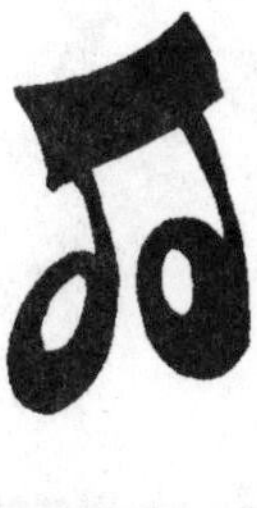

3. Try out your ideas. Which idea do you like best? Why?

____

____

____

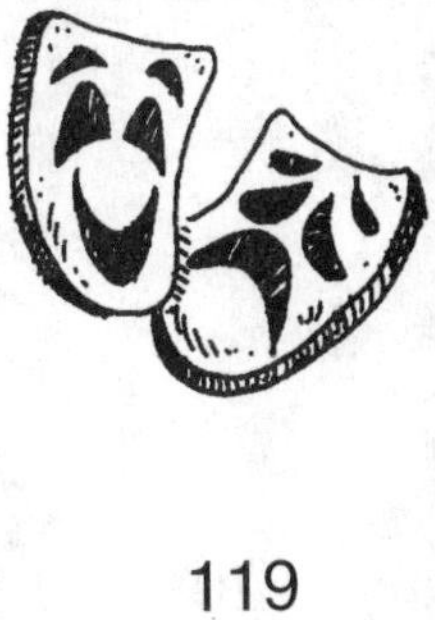

Arts (Dance) Objective: The student explores, discovers, and realizes multiple solutions to a given movement problem; chooses a favorite solution; and discusses the reasons for that choice.

Name_____ Date_____

Artists use curving and swirling lines to lead your eyes through an artwork and to create visual movement.

WHAT TO DO: Create an artwork that shows movement with curving and swirling lines.

1. Select the 🖌 tool and a color. Draw curving and swirling lines.

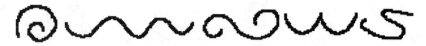

2. Use the 🖌 tool to draw a scene that shows excitement. Think of stormy weather, fireworks, or another exciting event. Choose a time of day.

Draw all objects and shapes with curved lines.

Use a variety of colors.

Technology Objective: The student uses software programs with graphics to enhance learning experiences.

120

TECHNOLOGY

Name_____ **Date**_____

PATTERNS REPEATING IN A POEM

Artwork often has visual motifs that repeat. A poem uses the sounds of language in a similar way. It uses repeating patterns in rhyme and rhythm. Words that *rhyme* have the same sound. *Rhythm* is a regular beat.

WHAT TO DO: Read this nursery rhyme out loud.

Baa, baa, black sheep,
Have you any wool?
Yes sir, yes sir,
Three bags full.

1. Write the two rhyming words.

_____   _____

Two lines in this poem have the same *rhythm*. This means that the lines have the same number of beats. They also have the same pattern of strong and weak beats. Write the lines that have the same rhythm.

_____

_____

Reading/Language Arts Objective: The student listens and responds to the musical elements of literary language (for example, cadence, pitch, onomatopoeia, rhyme).

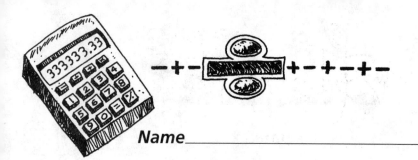

Name_____ Date_____

PATTERNS IN GROUPS OF NUMBERS

Repeating motifs are used in works of art. Groups of numbers can also have patterns. Think of the calendar. A week is seven days long. Suppose that today is May 1. Then, a week from today will be May 8 **(1 + 7 = 8)**. A week after that will be May 15 **(8 + 7 = 15)**.

WHAT TO DO: Look for a pattern in each row of numbers. If you find a pattern, describe it in a few words. If you do not find one, write **no pattern**. The first row is done for you.

1. 2   9   16   23   30

All the numbers are 7 apart.

2. 100   200   300   400   500

_____

3. 1   11   111   1,111   11,111

_____

4. 336   3   8   100   89

_____

5. 900   700   500   300   100

_____

Mathematics Objective: The student finds patterns in numbers.

Name _____   Date _____

WAVE PATTERNS

Many artworks show patterns that are found in nature–like waves, for example. A *wave* is a pattern of movement that repeats. Sound and light travel in waves that cannot be seen.

WHAT TO DO: Study the waves in each set. Find the pattern and continue it.

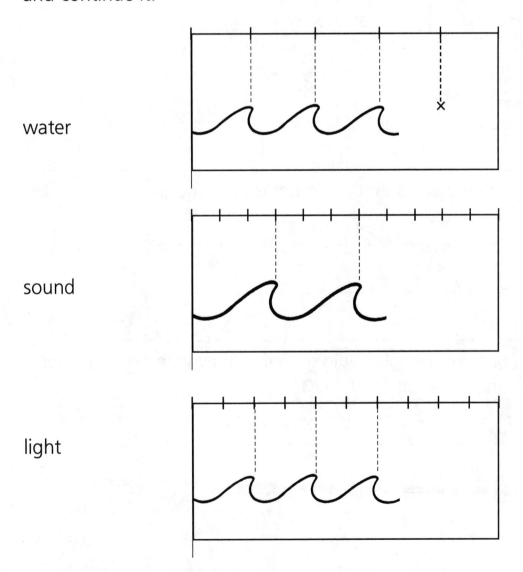

water

sound

light

Science Objective: The student interprets patterns that can be predicted, repeated, and copied.

SCIENCE

Name _____   Date _____

USING BEADS AS MONEY

In the past, some groups used beads as money. Today, we use coins and dollar bills as money, but we could use other objects.

WHAT TO DO: Answer the questions below.

1. Make a list of things we have to think about when we decide what is used as money.

_____

_____

_____

_____

2. List some objects that could be used as money.

_____

_____

_____

3. Tell one way people could get what they wanted or needed if money was not used.

_____

_____

_____

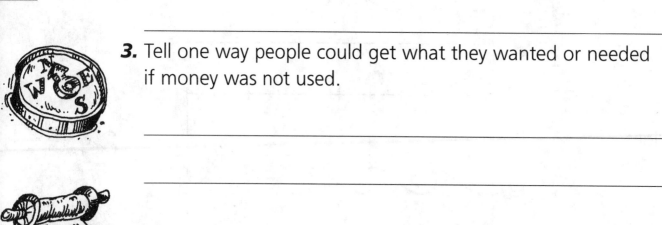

Social Studies Objectives: The student describes different ways people satisfy their needs and wants, past and present. The student describes the purpose of markets, where sellers compete to sell the same or similar products and buyers have choices.

SOCIAL STUDIES

Name _____ Date _____

PATTERNS AND DANCE

In math and in nature there are patterns or motifs. The numbers 2, 4, 6, and 8, for example, are a number pattern. Oak leaves and maple leaves each have a special shape or pattern to their leaves. A dance has a pattern, too. Certain steps can be repeated.

WHAT TO DO: Plan a dance. Write the steps. Repeat the steps. Plan two more steps and repeat them, and so on. Write your dance below.

1. _____

2. _____

(Repeat steps one and two.)

3. _____

4. _____

(Repeat steps three and four.)

5. _____

6. _____

(Repeat steps five and six.)

Arts (Dance) Objective: Create a dance project that reveals understanding of a concept or idea from another discipline (such as pattern in dance and science).

THE ARTS

Name _____ Date _____

A motif is one unit that is repeated to create a visual rhythm or pattern.

WHAT TO DO: Create visual rhythm by repeating a motif.

1. Select the ⬭ or ▭ shape tool and the ➘ tool. Design a motif. Combine geometric shapes of different sizes with straight lines.

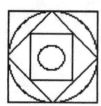  

2. Select three or four colors. Use the ◇ tool to fill the spaces of the motif.

3. Use the ✎ tool to select your motif. Choose Copy and then Paste from the Edit menu to create duplicates. Create a rhythm or pattern.

TECHNOLOGY

Name_____   Date_____

FINDING IDEAS TO WRITE ABOUT

Many artists use designs from nature to create an artwork.
You can take ideas from nature to use in stories.

WHAT TO DO: Think of an object in nature that you could
write about.

1. Draw a picture of the thing you chose.

2. Jot down words you could use to describe the object or
explain its purpose. Your ideas could be real or
make-believe.

_____

_____

_____

Reading/Language Arts Objective: The student generates ideas for writing by using prewriting techniques
(such as drawing, writing key thoughts).

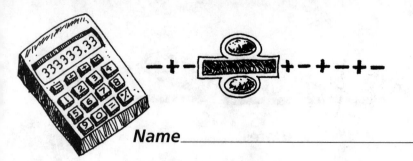

Name_____ Date_____

SHAPES EVERYWHERE

There are many repeating shapes in *Peony Blooms (IX)*. These shapes are free-form shapes. In our environment, we also have many geometric shapes.

WHAT TO DO: Complete the chart. Describe each shape. Then, tell where you see it in the classroom or in places outside the classroom.

Shape	Description	Location
circle		
rectangle		
triangle		

Mathematics Objective: The student identifies attributes of shapes and solids.

Name _____ Date _____

FLOWERS ATTRACT HELP

Artists often use flowers as designs. Bees and hummingbirds use flowers, too. They get food from flowers, and they help flowers by spreading pollen.

WHAT TO DO: Write **hummingbird** or **bee** to show which one would be attracted to each flower.

1.

2.

_____   _____

3.

4.

_____   _____

5.

_____

On the back of this paper, describe how a bee and flowers are designed to help each other.

Science Objectives: The student observes differences in the structures and functions of plants and animals.

SCIENCE

Name _____   Date _____

PLANTS FOR EVERYDAY USE

Most people like to look at pretty flowers. Plants are also used for food, clothing, and shelter.

WHAT TO DO: Under **Home,** write things you use at home that come from plants. Under **School**, write things you use at school that come from plants.

Home

_____

_____

_____

School

_____

_____

Tell which plant you think is most important and why.

_____

_____

_____

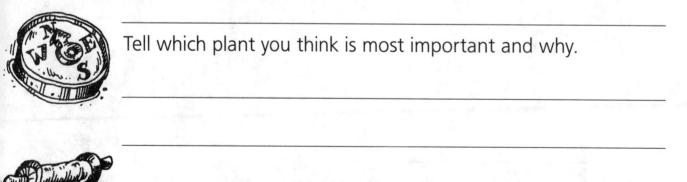

Social Studies Objective: The student discusses how one is a consumer of items in the home or school.

SOCIAL STUDIES

Name _____ Date _____

PATTERNS OF RHYTHM IN MUSIC

Artists repeat a motif to create rhythm in their art. Music has rhythm, too. Rhythm in music comes from the pattern of strong and weak beats. In most music, this pattern repeats again and again.

WHAT TO DO: Sing a favorite song or listen to a friend sing. Gently tap out the rhythm with your hand or foot. The beat pattern might look like one of these lines.

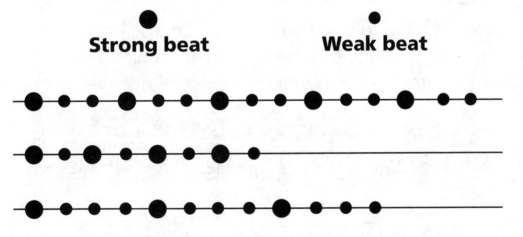

Strong beat   **Weak beat**

Write **X** in front of the line that shows the rhythm that is most like the one you tapped.

Now make up a new rhythm. Show it with weak and strong beats on the line below.

THE ARTS

Arts (Music) Objective: The student improvises simple rhythmic and melodic ostinato accompaniments.

Name_____ Date_____

A motif is repeated to create visual movement and rhythm.

WHAT TO DO: Create visual movement by repeating a motif made from free-form lines and shapes.

1. Select the 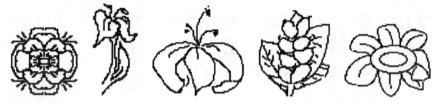 tool with a small brush. Draw a flower.

2. Use the ⌇ tool to select your flower. Choose Copy and then Paste from the Edit menu to create copies. Put them together in a way that creates visual rhythm.

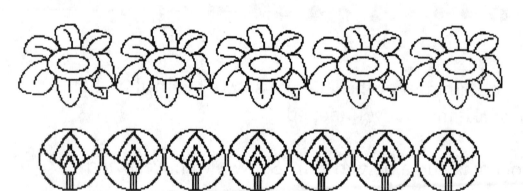

3. Use the 🖌 tool or the 🖉 tool to color the flowers. The colors should create a pattern.

Technology Objective: The student uses software programs with graphics to enhance learning experiences.

TECHNOLOGY

Name _____ Date _____

FORMS OF WORDS

In the lesson, you saw objects in nature that have patterns. Language also has patterns. Endings like *-ed* and *-ing* can be added to words to tell when something happened. These endings form a language pattern.

WHAT TO DO: Read the story about a class nature walk. In each sentence pair, a word is underlined in the first sentence. Use the correct form of that word to complete the second sentence.

1. We <u>walked</u> in the woods yesterday. Don't _____ there alone.

2. I saw the <u>biggest</u> snake ever. I can't tell you how

_____ it was.

3. It was <u>raining</u> yesterday. It didn't _____ on us.

4. We were <u>talking</u> too much on the trail. Our teacher

said not to _____ so much.

5. Sid <u>liked</u> the nature walk last year. He doesn't

_____ to walk now.

Reading/Language Arts Objective: The student decodes words with common inflections (such as *-ed*, *-ing*, *-est*).

Name_____ Date_____

CUTTING SHAPES OUT OF A CIRCLE

Do you see two circles in the picture of the tree and the moon? A circle can contain many interesting shapes.

WHAT TO DO: You will need scissors, a pencil, and a straight edge. What shapes can you find inside the circle?

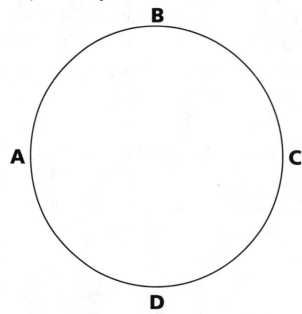

1. Draw a straight line from A to B.
2. Draw a straight line from B to C.
3. Draw a straight line from C to D.
4. Draw a straight line from D to A.
5. What shape did you make? Cut it out.
6. Label one corner of your shape A. Label the other corners B, C, and D in order.
7. Draw a straight line from A to C.
8. Draw a straight line from B to D.
9. What shapes did you make? How many?
10. Cut them out.

Mathematics Objective: The student cuts geometric shapes apart and identifies the new shapes made.

134

Name _____   Date _____

USING THINGS WISELY

Look at the picture of the big, round treetop in the art. Like the planet Earth, it is full of useful things. How could you use these things without using them up too fast?

WHAT TO DO: Each of the following things comes from the tree or from something that is in the tree. Write three ways that you could use each thing.

a bird's feather	a branch	a leaf

A thing that is *renewable* can be replaced with more of something. Are the things in the list above renewable?

_____

Science Objective: The student designs ways to conserve materials that come from the earth.

Name_____   Date_____

USING A GLOBE

Look at the picture of the tree and the moon. The artist of this picture is from the country of Iraq. Iraq is on the largest continent on the earth. That continent is called Asia.

WHAT TO DO: Look at the two sides of the globe below. Use a number from the list to label each ocean and each continent on this globe. Use maps, globes, or books if you need help.

SOCIAL STUDIES

1. Africa   **5.** Europe   **9.** Arctic Ocean
2. Antarctica   **6.** North America   **10.** Indian Ocean
3. Asia   **7.** South America   **11.** Pacific Ocean
4. Australia   **8.** Atlantic Ocean

Social Studies Objective: The student identifies major landforms and bodies of water on maps and globes.

Name _____ **Date** _____

CREATING CHARACTERS FOR A PLAY

The round treetop in the picture of the tree and moon seems full of birds. The birds are all different from each other.

WHAT TO DO: Choose three of the birds. Pretend that you will write a play about them. Give each bird a name and a personality. Describe how each bird would act.

1. Name: _____

_____

2. Name: _____

_____

3. Name: _____

_____

What do you think these birds would say to each other?
Write about what they might say.

4. _____

_____

5. _____

_____

6. _____

_____

Arts (Theater) Objectives: The student imagines and clearly describes characters, their relationships, and their environments.

THE ARTS

Name_____ Date_____

Many objects in nature have rhythms or patterns.
Artists draw patterns with lines and shapes.

WHAT TO DO: Draw a natural object with patterns.

1. Select the 🖌 tool with a small brush. Draw the shape of
something you can find in nature.

2. Add lines and shapes to the object to show patterns.

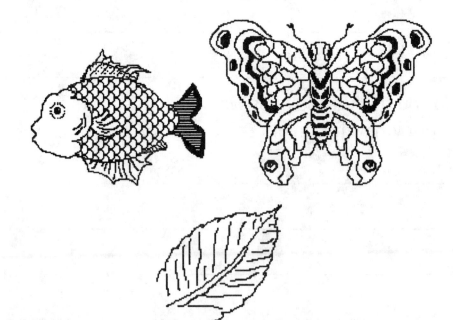

3. Add color to the object with the 🖌 tool or the ⬙ tool.

Technology Objective: The student uses software programs with graphics to enhance learning experiences.

TECHNOLOGY

Name _____ Date _____

INFERENCES

People read meanings into works of art such as *Dawn's Wedding Chapel II*. The same is true of a story. The writer might not tell you everything. You can figure out things from what you are told.

WHAT TO DO: Read the following story. Then, answer the questions.

When Jan got home from school, she saw a flower she wanted to pick. So Jan put her books down on the grass.

After dinner, rain fell in sheets. Mom said to Jan, "Let's work on that math problem now. Go get your math book."

Jan said, "I think I left it at school." But she had a worried look on her face.

1. Why did Jan have a worried look?_____

_____

2. Did Jan tell what really happened when she said her book

was at school? Explain. _____

_____

3. On the back of this paper, write an ending to the story.

Reading/Language Arts Objective: The student constructs and explains inferences (such as cause and effect, predictions, conclusions).

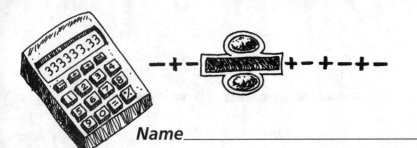

Name_____ Date_____

HUNDREDS, TENS, AND ONES

Louise Nevelson found many objects. She put them in boxes to make groups. Numbers have groups, too—groups of hundreds, tens, and ones. Below are blocks that show how to group numbers.

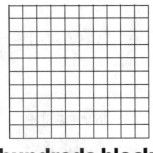 

hundreds block   **tens block**   **ones block**

WHAT TO DO: Each set of blocks shows a number. Write the number each set shows.

 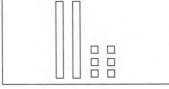 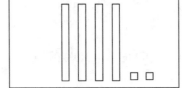 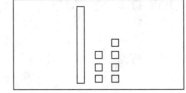

_____   _____   _____

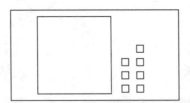 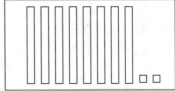

_____   _____

On the back of this paper, make the number 46 using number blocks.

Mathematics Objective: The student uses concrete models of hundreds, tens, and ones to represent, compare, and order whole numbers.

Name _____ **Date** _____

PUTTING THINGS IN ORDER

Artists put objects in a certain order to create visual patterns. Scientists put things in a certain order to study them.

WHAT TO DO: Number the following objects in order by weight, from lightest to heaviest.

A.   **B.**  **C.** **D.**

SCIENCE

_____ _____ _____ _____

Put the following objects in order by temperature, from coldest to hottest.

E. **F.** 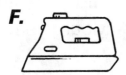 **G.** **H.**

_____ _____ _____ _____

Tell why a scientist might order things by weight or by temperature.

_____

_____

_____

Science Objective: The student identifies the purpose of meaningfully ordered objects.

Name _____ Date _____

WHEN DID IT HAPPEN?

Artists put objects in a certain order to create visual patterns. History helps us learn the order in which things happened in the past.

WHAT TO DO: The following is the story of a president of the United States. The events are not in order. Number the sentences to show the order in which the events occurred.

_____ **A.** He became the first president of the United States.

_____ **B.** As a young man, he helped run his family's farm.

_____ **C.** He was born in Virginia in 1732.

_____ **D.** He was president for eight years; then, he retired to his home at Mount Vernon.

Who was this president? Write his name on the line.

_____

Social Studies Objective: The student, on listening to or reading historical stories, myths, and narratives, can place events about the past in the correct sequence.

SOCIAL STUDIES

Name _____ Date _____

A STAGE FOR A PLAY

The boxes in *Dawn's Wedding Chapel II* are like little stages. In each box, you see interesting things–just as you would see in a play on a stage.

The objects on a stage can show where the action takes place. They can also help set a mood or feeling.

WHAT TO DO: For each play, write at least two things that you would put on the stage. On the back of this page, draw a detailed picture for one of the plays.

1. a play about circus performers

_____

_____

2. a play about life 100 years ago

_____

_____

3. a play about life in a space colony

_____

_____

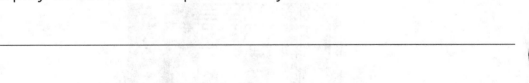

THE ARTS

Arts (Theater) Objective: The student visualizes environments and constructs designs to communicate locale and mood using visual elements (such as space, color, line, shape, texture) and aural aspects using a variety of sound sources.

Name _____ **Date** _____

Artists arrange found objects to create visual rhythms or patterns.

WHAT TO DO: Create a box design with visual patterns.

1. Select the ☐ shape tool and draw a large rectangle or square that fills the screen.

2. Create different spaces for patterns with the ➜ tool or the ☐ or ⬭ shape tools.

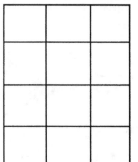 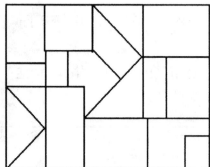

3. Look around the classroom and find objects to draw in each section. Alternate drawings of objects with patterns you create. Fill all the spaces.
Select from a variety of tools: ☐ ⬭ 🖌 ✒ ➜
Use the ✋ tool and the pattern selections.

Technology Objective: The student uses software programs with graphics to enhance learning experiences.

144

TECHNOLOGY

Name_____ Date_____

MAKING SENTENCES BALANCE

When an object has formal balance, both sides match. When you write a sentence, both parts of the sentence must match, too, like in these sentences:

The girl eats an apple.   The boys eat bananas.

WHAT TO DO: Write a sentence using each word below.

1. bakes

_____

2. brings

_____

3. help

_____

4. play

_____

5. like

_____

6. jump

_____

7. runs

_____

8. climbs

_____

Reading/Language Arts Objective: The student uses conventions of grammar and usage (including subject-verb agreement, plurals, verb tenses).

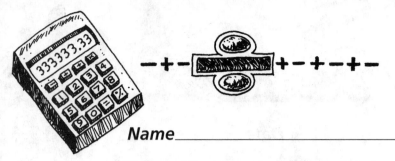

Name_____   Date_____

BALANCING FIGURES

If you look at the Chinese food container, you will see that the shape and the designs are the same on both sides. When both halves of a figure are exactly the same, the object has formal balance.

WHAT TO DO: Finish drawing each figure. Use the broken line as the center line.

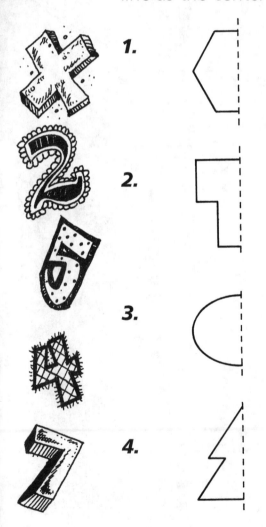

1.

2.

3.

4.

Mathematics Objective: The student identifies attributes of shapes and solids.

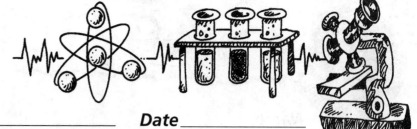

Name _____   Date _____

LIVING AND NONLIVING THINGS

The Chinese probably put fruit or rice in the food container.
Fruit and rice come from plants, which are living things. The
container is made of metal. Metal is a nonliving thing.

WHAT TO DO: Read the list below. Decide whether each word
names a living or a nonliving thing. Then, write each word in
the correct column.

desk	daisy	apple	pencil	table	fork
bird	turtle	shoe	corn	puppy	chair

Living things   **Nonliving things**

_____   _____

_____   _____

_____   _____

_____   _____

_____   _____

Make your own list of living and nonliving things.

Living things   **Nonliving things**

_____   _____

_____   _____

_____   _____

Science Objective: The student compares and contrasts biological and nonbiological objects from the past and
present (biological to biological, nonbiological to nonbiological, and biological to nonbiological).

147

Name_____ Date_____

FINDING FACTS

The Chinese food container was made by an artist who lived in China long ago. You can learn interesting facts about China from different sources. Maps, encyclopedias, and dictionaries can be used.

WHAT TO DO: Read the questions. Write **map, encyclopedia,** or **dictionary** to tell where to find the information.

1. What language do the people of China speak?

_____

2. What is the main crop of China?_____

3. What countries are near China?_____

4. What does *container* mean?_____

5. What is the capital of China?_____

6. What ocean is east of China? _____

7. What is the population of China? _____

8. What is the longest river in China?_____

9. What are the three largest cities in China?

_____

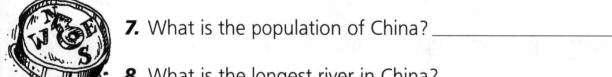

Social Studies Objective: The student names several sources of information about a period or event.

SOCIAL STUDIES

Name _____ **Date** _____

WRITING A DIALOGUE

The artist made the food container so that two sides are alike. In a play, a conversation between two or more characters is a dialogue. Dialogue is written like this:

Little Red Riding Hood: Granny, what big ears you have!

Wolf: All the better to hear you with.

WHAT TO DO: Write a dialogue.

(Character 1) _____ :

_____

_____

(Character 2) _____ :

_____

_____

(Character 1) _____ :

_____

_____

(Character 2) _____ :

_____

_____

THE ARTS

Arts (Theater) Objective: The student improvises dialogue to tell stories, and formalizes improvisation by writing or recording the dialogue.

Name_____ **Date**_____

Formal balance means both halves of an object are the same.

WHAT TO DO: Design a container with formal balance.

1. Select the ✏ tool and draw a pot, vase, jar, or bowl with handles. Use the Brush Mirrors command from the Options menu, if available.

2. Use the same tool to add lines and shapes to create patterns. Make the patterns the same on both sides.

3. Select the ✋ tool and some colors. Add color so that both sides continue to match.

Technology Objective: The student uses software programs with graphics to enhance learning experiences.

Name _____ Date_____

USING A GLOSSARY

In a book about ancient Egypt, you might see words you do not know. You could find the words' meanings in a glossary at the back of the book or in a dictionary.

papyrus A riverbank reed that the ancient Egyptians used to make paper.

sarcophagus An elaborately decorated case for a mummy.

sphinx A statue having the body of a lion and the head of a person.

WHAT TO DO: Use the glossary to answer each question.

1. What did the Egyptians make paper from?

_____

2. What is a statue with the body of a lion and the head of

a person called? _____

3. What was a mummy placed in?

_____

Use a dictionary to write a definition for each word.

4. pyramid _____

_____

5. scribe _____

_____

Reading/Language Arts Objective: The student uses resources and references (such as beginners' dictionaries, glossaries, available technology) to determine word meanings.

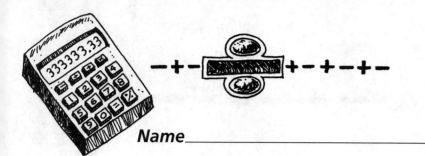

Name_____ Date_____

TELLING TIME

People throughout the ages have used different instruments to tell time. In Egypt, where the mummy case was found, a sundial was used to tell time. Now people use clocks to tell time.

WHAT TO DO: Read each clock and write the time.

1. _____

2. _____

3. _____

4. _____

5. _____

Mathematics Objective: The student uses hours and minutes to describe the time shown on a clock.

Name_____ Date_____

CYCLES AND PATTERNS IN NATURE

There are many cycles and patterns in nature. The mummy case reminds us of the human life cycle. We are born, we grow up and live our lives, and we die. There are other cycles and patterns in nature, too. The food chain is a pattern. Plants use sunlight to grow, animals eat plants, other animals eat the plant-eaters or use things the animals produce.

WHAT TO DO: Look at the pictures. Complete each sentence. Explain how each thing pictured is part of a pattern.

The sun _____

_____

The plants _____

_____

The cow _____

_____

The children _____

_____

153

Name _____   **Date** _____

LAWS AND RULES

Rules and laws were important in ancient Egyptian society, and they are important today. Rules and laws help keep order, provide safety, and solve arguments.

WHAT TO DO: Write some rules or laws that you know about. Follow the directions.

1. Write one rule that will help keep order in your classroom.

_____

2. Write one rule that will help keep order in your school.

_____

3. Write one law that will help keep you safe in the car.

_____

4. Write one rule that will help you stay safe on your bicycle.

_____

5. Write one law that will keep a pet dog safe.

_____

6. Write one rule that helps solve arguments in your family.

_____

Social Studies Objective: The student identifies laws and rules which establish order, provide security, and manage conflict.

SOCIAL STUDIES

Name _____ Date _____

MAKING A DANCE FOR A SPECIAL OCCASION

In ancient Egypt, dance was an important part of religious events and other special occasions. Dancers often wore masks that represented animals or gods. You can see figures of dancers painted on tombs and burial cases.

WHAT TO DO: Think of an occasion that you can create a dance for.

1. Tell about a special time when people might dance.

_____

2. Will the music for your dance be fast or slow?

_____

3. Write the steps for your dance. Be sure to tell which way to move: *Hop to the left*.

a. _____

b. _____

c. _____

d. _____

4. Practice the dance. On the back, write what works and what does not work. Tell how to fix the dance.

_____

_____

_____

THE ARTS

Arts (Dance) Objectives: The student accurately demonstrates eight basic locomotor movements (such as walk, run, hop, jump, leap, gallop, slide, and skip), traveling forward, backward, sideward, diagonally, and turning. The student improves and performs dances based on their own ideas and concepts from other sources.

Name_____ Date_____

Formal balance, or symmetry, is found in many objects, including our bodies.

WHAT TO DO: Design a symmetrical sarcophagus.

1. Use the ▣ tool to draw a symmetrical mummy case. Use the Brush Mirrors command from the Options menu, if available.

2. Add lines and shapes. Match the patterns on both sides. Use the Brush Mirrors command, if available.

3. Use the ▧ tool to add color. Match color on both sides.

Technology Objective: The student uses software programs with graphics to enhance learning experiences.

TECHNOLOGY

Name_____   Date_____

DRAWING CONCLUSIONS

Suppose you were in a room with a table and chairs, a stove, and a refrigerator. The objects in the room plus your experience would help you draw a conclusion, or figure out, that the room is a kitchen. You draw conclusions when you read, too.

WHAT TO DO: Read the sentences. Answer the question. Underline the clues.

1. The leaves were turning colors. The days were getting shorter. Juan put on a jacket when he went out. What season was it?

_____

2. Mom made a chocolate cake. Everyone sang. Tia blew out

candles. What day was it?_____

3. It was Saturday afternoon. Terri stood in line. She bought a box of popcorn. She got to her seat just as the lights went

out. Where was Terri?_____

4. Ann put her clothes into the suitcase. She made sure she had her plane ticket. She could hardly wait to see Grandma and Grandpa. What was Ann going to do?

_____

Reading/Language Arts Objective: The student constructs and explains inferences (such as cause and effect, predictions, conclusions).

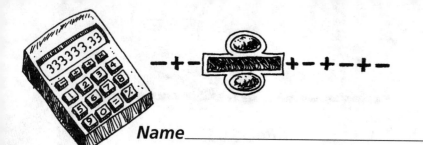

Name_____ Date_____

PICTOGRAPHS

Some sidechairs are very special—one-of-a-kind. There are many chairs in a school, and most of them are alike. The pictograph below shows how many chairs were in rooms of a make-believe school.

Chairs in Red Oaks School

Each stands for 5 chairs.

First Grade   **Second Grade**   **Third Grade**

Fourth Grade   **Fifth Grade**

WHAT TO DO: Use the pictograph to answer the questions.

1. How many chairs are there in each classroom?

First Grade _____   Fourth Grade_____

Second Grade_____   Fifth Grade _____

Third Grade_____

2. Which classroom has the most chairs?_____

3. Which has the fewest chairs?_____

4. How many more chairs are there in fifth grade than in

the third grade?_____

Mathematics Objective: The student draws conclusions and answers questions based on graphed data.

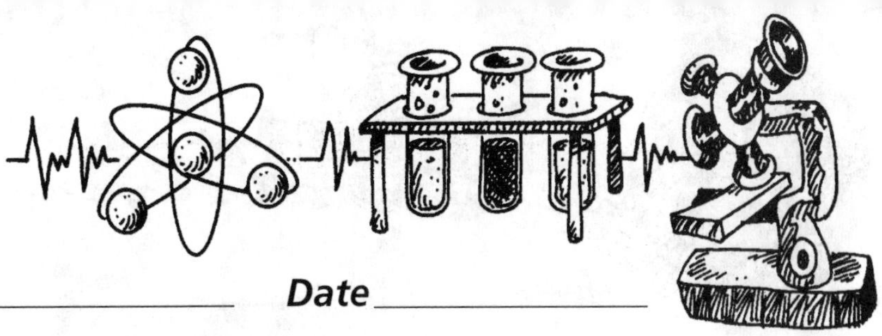

Name_____ Date_____

SAFETY AT HOME AND IN SCHOOL

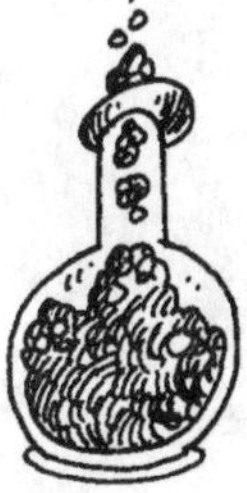

When artists build furniture, such as the chair in the lesson, they use many kinds of tools. Before they use a new tool, they read the directions and learn how to use it correctly and safely.

WHAT TO DO: Read the sentences. Write two safety rules that the person should follow in each situation.

1. Peter is cooking spaghetti for dinner._____

_____

_____

2. You are riding your bike to a friend's house._____

_____

_____

3. David walks to school each morning._____

_____

_____

4. Anna rides the bus to school each day._____

_____

_____

5. You are taking a bath._____

_____

_____

Science Objective: The student observes and follows home and school safety procedures.

Name _____ Date _____

COMPARING THE CITY AND THE COUNTRY

The sidechair in the lesson would fit in a home in an urban are or in a rural area. An *urban area* is a city or town. A farm or small village is a *rural area*.

WHAT TO DO: Think about how urban and rural areas are alike and different. Look at each picture. Write **urban** or **rural** to tell what area the picture shows.

1.

2.

_____   _____

3. Some people like to live in a rural area. Some like to like in an urban area. Write a good reason for living in a city.

_____

Write a good reason for living in the country.

_____

Social Studies Objective: The student distinguishes between urban and rural.

SOCIAL STUDIES

Name _____ **Date** _____

STATIONARY BODY MOVEMENT

Did you know that sometimes dancers perform sitting down?
Actions like stretching and bending are *stationary movements*,
performed when the dancer remains in one place.

WHAT TO DO: Follow the directions below.

1. Practice the following movements while sitting in a chair:

| stretch | twist | turn |
| bend | wiggle | twirl |

2. Which ones can be easily done in a chair?

_____

3. Use a word from above to describe one way each body
part can move.

a. arm _____

b. leg _____

c. head _____

d. shoulder _____

e. finger _____

f. waist _____

THE ARTS

Arts (Dance) Objective: The student accurately demonstrates nonlocomotor/axial movements (such as bend,
twist, stretch, swing).

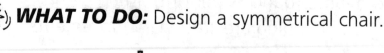
Name _____ **Date** _____

Furniture has formal balance to match our bodies.

WHAT TO DO: Design a symmetrical chair.

1. Select the 🖌 tool or the ⬭ or ☐ shape tool Draw a symmetrical chair. Use the Brush Mirrors command from the Options menu, if available.

2. Add interesting features to your chair.

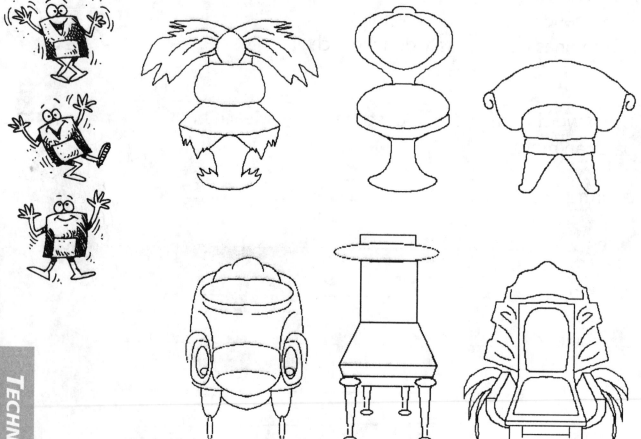

3. Use the 🖌 tool to add color to your chair.

Technology Objective: The student uses software programs with graphics to enhance learning experiences.

TECHNOLOGY

162

Name_____   Date_____

STAR WORDS

Many people saw the bright shower of falling stars that the artist pictured in the quilt . For thousands of years, people have watched the sky. Some words used to talk about objects in the sky are very old. For example, *Sol* is from Latin, the language of ancient Rome. *Sol* means "sun." *Astron* is from the Greek language. *Astron* means "star."

WHAT TO DO: Use the meanings above to help you choose the word that completes each sentence. Write the correct word in the blank.

1. An_____is someone who studies the stars. (astronomer, solstice)

2. We ate breakfast in the_____ , a sunny room. (asteroid, solarium)

3. The sun is at the center of the _____ system. (astral, solar)

4. The day with the most hours of sunlight marks the summer _____ north of the equator. (solstice, astronomy)

5. Many_____are found between the planets Mars and Jupiter. (solariums, asteroids)

Reading/Language Arts Objective: The student applies meanings of word parts to determine word meaning.

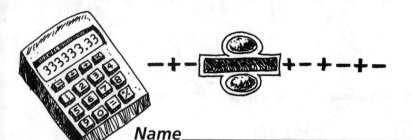

Name_____   Date_____

TO THE MOON AND BACK

The quilt in the lesson shows stars shooting through the sky. Stars are many millions of miles from Earth. Even Earth's closest neighbors in the solar system are very far away. Scientists use large numbers to show these distances.

Knowing place values can help you write large numbers. Each place value greater than the ones place has a certain number of zeros.

Tens	Hundreds	Thousands	Ten Thousands	Hundred Thousands	Millions	Ten Millions	Hundred Millions
10	100	1,000	10,000	100,000	1,000,000	10,000,000	100,000,000

WHAT TO DO: Write the highest place value shown in each number.

Place Value

1. Earth to the moon   239,000 miles _____

2. Earth to the sun   93,000,000 miles _____

3. Earth to Venus   160,000,000 miles _____

4. Earth around equator   24, 900 miles _____

5. North Pole to South Pole   7,900 miles

6. Write the numbers in order from largest to smallest.

_____

_____

_____

_____

Mathematics Objective: The student uses patterns in place value to compare and order whole numbers.

Name _____ Date _____

COMETS

Falling stars like the ones shown on the quilt in the lesson
are really pieces of stone or metal from outer space. The
pieces sometimes come from the tails of comets. *Comets* look
like fuzzy stars to us. Comets *orbit*, or circle, the sun, just as
the planets do. Some comets have short orbits that last only
a few years. Other comets may take hundreds or thousands
of years to orbit the sun.

WHAT TO DO: Look at the name of each comet, the time of
its orbit around the sun, and the date when seen. Use the time
of the orbit to find out the dates when the comet was or will
next be seen.

SCIENCE

Comet	Orbit Time	Sighting	Next Sighting
1. Halley	76 years	1910	_____
2. Encke	3 years	1786	_____
3. Great Comet	513 years	1843	_____
4. Pons-Winnecke	6 years	1819	_____
5. Schwassmann-Wachmann	15 years	1925	_____

Science Objective: The student identifies, predicts, and compares events and objects that appear in patterns.

Name_____ Date_____

QUILTING BEES

Quilts like the one in the lesson are warm coverings for beds, and they are beautiful, too. Long ago, colonial women made quilts at *quilting bees*. As they quilted, the women talked. The quilting bees gave them a chance to build friendships and to help one another.

WHAT TO DO: Think of a group that you belong to. It could be a family, a group of friends, a class, a club, or a sports team. Describe how members of your group help one another.

_____

_____

_____

_____

_____

_____

_____

_____

_____

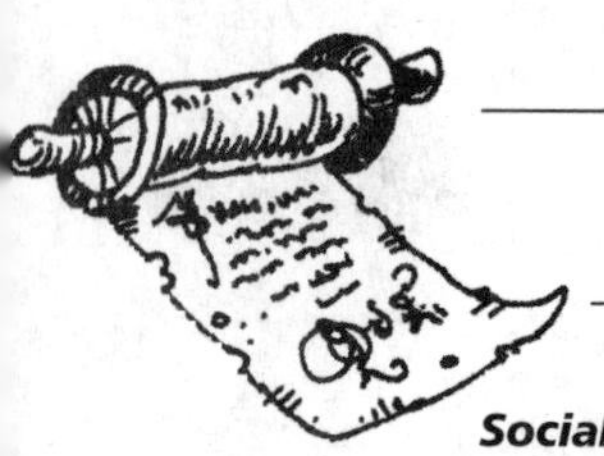

Social Studies Objective: The student identifies roles, duties, and responsibilities in group settings.

Name _____ Date _____

THE EXCITEMENT OF DISCOVERY

The quilt in the lesson was made to remind people of the night stars fell. Look at the shapes of the people on the quilt. Were the people excited?

WHAT TO DO: Imagine that you and a friend have just discovered a new planet. Use your name and your friend's name. Write your conversation and describe your gestures or actions.

Character's Name	Dialog	Gestures/ Actions

THE ARTS

Arts (Theater) Objective: The student improvises dialogue to tell stories, and formalizes improvisations by writing or recording the dialogue.

Name_____ **Date**_____

Artists sometimes create tactile and visual texture in sticheries.

WHAT TO DO: Create an artwork that looks like a stitchery.

1. Select the 🖌 tool or the ➘ tool. Draw a favorite object with broken lines.

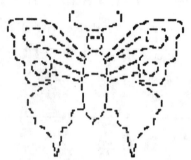

2. Draw another object with a solid line. Use the ✐ tool to erase parts of the line to look like stitching.

3. Add a background to complete your stitchery design. Use either method to draw broken lines.

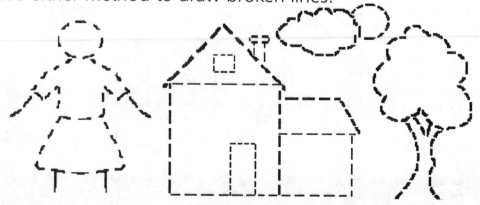

Technology Objective: The student uses software programs with graphics to enhance learning experiences.

168

TECHNOLOGY

Name _____   Date_____

WEAVING WORDS TOGETHER

The weaver of the *Osage Sash* changed the texture of the cloth by changing the way yarns were woven together. Writers can change the way they tell something by changing the ways they build sentences. You can change the structure of sentences by moving their parts.

The rescuers searched for the boat *after the storm passed*. *After the storm passed*, the rescuers searched for the boat.

WHAT TO DO: Rewrite the sentences. Change the structure of each sentence.

1. Jason will play in the game tomorrow._____

_____

2. A cool breeze blew outside the window._____

_____

3. Before breakfast, Clare made her bed._____

_____

4. We heard a howl in the middle of the night._____

_____

5. On the table, there was a small clock._____

_____

Reading/Language Arts Objective: The student writes in complete sentences, varying sentence structure as appropriate to meaning and audience.

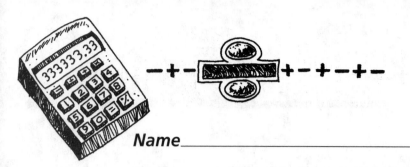

Name_____ Date_____

USING SETS TO SOLVE PROBLEMS

The weaver of the *Osage Sash* worked with sets of yarns to make the patterns in the sash. You can use number patterns to find how many parts you need to build something.

WHAT TO DO: Draw pictures to help solve the problems. Then write the number sentence for each problem.

1. Keith works at a factory that builds bicycles. How many wheels does he need to build three bicycles?

_____

2. How many wheels will it take to make four bicycles?

_____

3. How many wheels would it take to make six bicycles?

_____

Mathematics Objective: The student generates a list of paired numbers based on a given real-life situation such as number of tricycles related to number of wheels.

Name _____   Date _____

EARTH TEXTURES

Like the *Osage Sash*, the earth has texture. Landforms give the earth its texture. Some landforms are high, and some are low. Some landforms are smooth, and some are rough.

WHAT TO DO: Read the names of different landforms. Use words below to tell what the landform is. If you need help, look up the names of the landforms in a dictionary or encyclopedia.

swamp   canyon   desert   lake   river
mountain   waterfall   cave   volcano   prairie

SCIENCE

1. Everest _____

2. Gobi _____

3. Niagara _____

4. Tanganyika _____

5. Nile _____

6. Royal Gorge _____

7. Carlsbad Caverns _____

8. Everglades _____

9. Mauna Loa _____

10. Pampas _____

Science Objective: The student sorts and analyzes objects according to like properties.

Name _____   Date _____

READING THE PAST

Objects like the *Osage Sash* tell us a great deal about the
people who made them. You can study the details of these
objects to learn more about their makers. For example, the yarn
in the sash may tell us whether the people grew crops like cotton
or raised sheep for wool. The yarn can also tell us whether the
people used *dyes* made from plants to color their clothing.

WHAT TO DO: Look around the room for examples of clocks
and watches. Study the details of the clocks or watches. Tell
how the objects are alike and how they are different.

_____

_____

_____

_____

Look at the picture. Do you know
what this is? Do you know what it
was used for in the past? Ask an
adult at home whether he or she
can tell you. Write your answers.

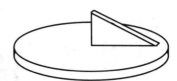

What is it?_____

What was it used for ?_____

Social Studies Objective: The student uses evidence such as photographs and interviews to compare various
interpretations of the same time period.

SOCIAL STUDIES

Name _____ Date _____

DRESSING THE PART

The *Osage Sash* was a part of someone's *wardrobe*, or set of clothing. In a play, actors wear clothing that fit in with the characters they are playing. This clothing is called a *costume*.

WHAT TO DO: Think of a story you have read that would make a good play. Choose a character you would like to be. Then write your answers to the questions.

1. Write the name of your character. _____

2. What role does your character play? For example, is your

character a cook or a dragon or an astronaut?_____

_____

3. Make a list of all the things your character will need for a

costume._____

_____

_____

4. Draw a picture of your character in costume.

THE ARTS

Arts (Theater) Objective: The student imagines and clearly describes characters, their relationships, and their environments.

Name_____ **Date**_____

Artists use color, shape, or texture to emphasize an area in an artwork.

WHAT TO DO: Create a design with emphasis in one area.

1. Select the 🖌 tool or the ✏ tool. Draw several small animal shapes.

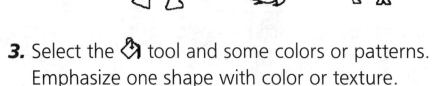

2. Use the ⌴ tool to select your shapes. Choose the Copy and Paste commands from the Edit menu to create copies. Arrange the shapes to make a pleasing design. If you wish, use commands from the Selection menu to rotate a selected shape.

3. Select the 🪣 tool and some colors or patterns. Emphasize one shape with color or texture.

TECHNOLOGY

Technology Objective: The student uses software programs with graphics to enhance learning experiences.

174

Name_____ Date_____

DESCRIBING HOW THINGS FEEL

Virginia Caswell used different kinds of materials to make her mask. You can imagine the texture of the mask. You might use words like *smooth*, *bumpy*, or *prickly* to tell how the mask feels. Words that tell how things feel are called *describing words*, or *adjectives*.

WHAT TO DO: Choose a word from below to describe how each thing feels. More than one word might be work.

cold   sticky   smooth   wet   furry   hot

1. glue _____

2. kitten _____

3. snow _____

4. sun _____

5. glass _____

6. water _____

Describe the texture of each pictured object.

7. _____

_____

8. _____

_____

Reading/Language Arts Objective: The student develops vocabulary through concrete and multisensory experiences.

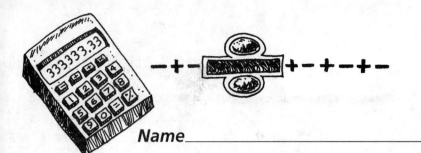

Name_____ Date_____

DRAWING A PICTURE TO SOLVE A PROBLEM

Artists make masks, such as the one in the lesson, for different reasons: for creative expression, for dancers to wear, or for holiday celebrations.

Sue made masks for her classmates to wear for a play. She made one mask on Monday, two Tuesday, and three Wednesday. Sue continued this pattern for five days. How many masks did she make?

WHAT TO DO: Draw a picture to help solve the problem. Draw a circle to show each mask that Sue made.

Monday: ◯

Tuesday: ◯ ◯

Wednesday:

Thursday:

Friday:

Sue made _____ masks.

Draw pictures on the back of this paper to solve this problem: How many cans did Bill collect if he gathered twice as many as the day before for each of four days. On the first day he found 6 cans.

Mathematics Objective: To solve problems, the student selects or develops an appropriate problem-solving strategy, including draw a picture, look for a pattern, systematic guess and check, or act it out.

Name_____ Date_____

MASKED ANIMALS

A *raccoon* has a band of black hair around its eyes. It looks like it's wearing a furry mask. Raccoons live in the woods. They eat fruit, nuts, seeds, and other small animals. They hunt at night. Raccoons are good climbers because they have strong, flexible fingers and sharp claws.

A *giant panda* has a white, chubby body with black legs, and a black patch around each eye. It also looks like it's wearing a mask. Pandas live in the forests of China. Pandas use their paws like fingers to peel the leaves of the bamboo shoots that they eat. The panda is active at night.

WHAT TO DO: Write the words that tell about the raccoon in the circle on the left. Write about the giant panda in the circle on the right. Write about both animals where the circles overlap.

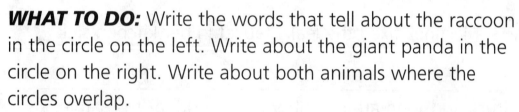

Raccoon	Both	Panda

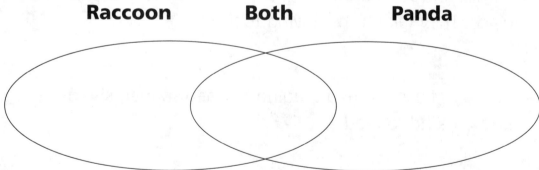

eats bamboo   eats fruit, nuts, small animals
hunts at night   furry body
mask-like face   uses front paws like fingers
lives in forests

Science Objective: The student observes differences in the structures and functions of plants and animals.

Name _____ **Date** _____

PROTECTING THE ENVIRONMENT

Virginia Caswell used materials that she found in her environment to make a mask. When you use materials again instead of throwing them away, you *recycle* them. When you use natural resources like water, land, or fuel wisely, you *conserve* them.

WHAT TO DO: Write *recycling* or *conserving* to describe what each person is doing.

1. Mike separates aluminum cans from the other garbage and takes them to a special center.

_____

2. Mrs. Martinez fixed the leaky faucet in her kitchen sink.

_____

3. Patrick and John are neighbors who work at the same place. They take turns driving to work.

_____

4. When Katie is finished reading her newspaper, she gives it to a friend to read.

_____

5. List three things that can be recycled.

a. _____

b. _____

c. _____

Social Studies Objective: The student identifies actions that can protect the environment (for example, recycling, conserving, and replenishing).

SOCIAL STUDIES

Name _____ **Date** _____

MUSICAL INSTRUMENTS

Masks are used in celebrations throughout the world. Music is often an important part of a celebration also. People use many different kinds of instruments to make music.

WHAT TO DO: Think about sounds that different musical instruments make. Tell how each kind of instrument's sound is made.

1. Stringed Instruments _____

2. Wind Instruments _____

3. Percussion Instruments _____

Classify the instruments. Write each name under the heading that shows the kind of instrument it is.

cymbals	harp	piano
trumpet	drum	saxophone
flute	tuba	tambourine
violin	guitar	triangle

Stringed Instruments	**Wind Instruments**	**Percussion Instruments**
_____	_____	_____
_____	_____	_____
_____	_____	_____
_____	_____	_____

THE ARTS

Arts (Music) Objective: The student uses appropriate terminology in explaining music, music notation, music instruments, and voices, and music performances.

Name_____ Date_____

Artists use texture and formal balance in masks.

WHAT TO DO: Create a mask design with formal balance and texture.

1. Use the 🖌 tool to draw a large mask shape. Use the Brush Mirrors command from the Option menu, if available.

2. Think of a mood. Add interesting features. Make sure your mask has formal balance.

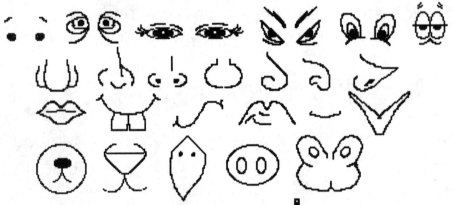

3. Use the ✋ tool, the ✏ tool, or the 🖌 tool to add color and texture to the spaces. Think of natural materials. Continue to show formal balance.

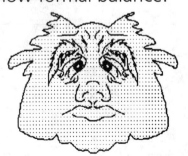

Technology Objective: The student uses software programs with graphics to enhance learning experiences.

180

TECHNOLOGY

Name _____ Date _____

Up or Down?

Look at the painting, *The Tree of Houses*. Do you see a lot of up-and-down motion? The trees seem to stretch to the sky. But, look carefully! Do you see a bird swooping down?

WHAT TO DO: The underlined word in each sentence describes a motion up or down. Other words in the sentence give you clues to the direction. Write **up** if the word tells about moving up. Write **down** if it tells about moving down.

_____ **1.** Watch the bird <u>soar</u> high.

_____ **2.** The falling tree will <u>plunge</u> to the ground.

_____ **3.** The bird fished above the <u>crest</u> of the wave.

_____ **4.** The moon <u>dipped</u> low in the sky.

Now write a sentence using one of the *up* words. Then, write another sentence using one of the *down* words.

5. up: _____

_____

6. down: _____

_____

Reading/Language Arts Objective: The student develops vocabulary through reading.

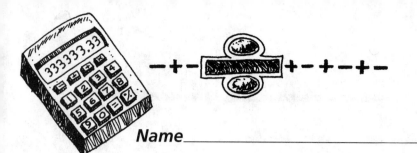

Name_____ Date_____

Adding Many Times

Look at the ladders in *The Tree of Houses*. A ladder has rungs for climbing up and down. How many steps does this ladder have?

WHAT TO DO: Fill in the numbers to write the number sentences that tell about the pictures.

1. You have two ladders that are alike. How many rungs are there all together?

_____ + _____ = _____

2. If you have three ladders, how many rungs will you have all together?

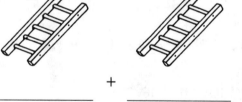

_____ + _____ + _____ = _____

3. On the back of this paper, draw four ladders with five rungs each. Write a number sentence to show how many rungs there are all together.

Mathematics Objective: The student models, creates, and describes a problem situation in which equivalent sets of concrete objects are joined or formed.

Name _____ Date _____

Patterns in Nature

Artists repeat patterns to create harmony in their work. There are repeating patterns in nature, also.

WHAT TO DO: Each picture shows a repeating pattern. Under each picture, tell what the pattern is. Then, draw a picture to show what comes next in the pattern.

1.

_____

2.

_____

3.

_____

Science Objective: The student identifies, predicts, and compares events and objects that appear in patterns.

SCIENCE

Name _____ **Date** _____

Rules to Live By

In Paul Klee's painting, you see a giant tree with houses on its branches. Think how the people who live in these houses might get along, sharing one tree.

WHAT TO DO: People need rules in order to live together peacefully. Imagine that you live in the house of trees. Put an **X** beside each rule that will be helpful to you and your neighbors. Then, answer the question.

_____ **1.** Throw garbage out the window of your tree house.

_____ **2.** Clean up dead limbs and leaves.

_____ **3.** Keep making your house bigger and bigger.

_____ **4.** Warn people around you if you see a thief.

_____ **5.** Remove a ladder whenever you feel like it.

_____ **6.** Play music so loudly that it shakes the tree.

_____ **7.** Let your children play wherever they want to.

_____ **8.** Vote on adding a grocery store.

9. What special problems might you have in a tree house? How might the people in the tree houses decide what rules they need? Write your ideas on the back of this page.

SOCIAL STUDIES

Name _____   Date _____

Arrange Music

In *The Tree of Houses,* the painter repeats similar shapes. In music, we repeat similar parts called *phrases.* Think of songs you know. In most of them, one phrase of music equals one line of the words to the song. Think of a song, such as "Row, Row, Row Your Boat." Imagine that four people are going to sing it as a round. You are the arranger. Who will start? Where will you add musical instruments?

WHAT TO DO: Below are some musical phrases and one way you might combine them to sing the song. Put the phrases together in a different way to create a pleasing song. Use the example as you write your arrangement.

Musical Phrases

1	Voice melody A	**5**	Drum roll
2	Voice melody B	**6**	Cymbal crash
3	Voice melody C	**7**	Bell ring
4	Voice melody D	**8**	Flute solo

Example: **5** → **1** → **2** → **1** → **5**

Your arrangement:

_____

THE ARTS

Arts (Music) Objectives: The student identifies the sounds of a variety of instruments, as well as children's voices; The student identifies ways in which the principles and subject matter of other disciplines taught in the school are interrelated with those of music.

Name_____ Date_____

Artists repeat parts of objects and colors to create harmony in an artwork.

WHAT TO DO: Create harmony in a design by using similar shapes and colors.

1. Select from a variety of tools: Draw a free-form or geometric object.

2. Draw similar objects in a variety of sizes. Use similar shapes.

3. Use the tool to fill the design with color. Create harmony with related colors, like reds and oranges or blues and greens.

Technology Objective: The student uses software programs with graphics to enhance learning experiences.

186

Name _____ Date _____

Why Do We Listen?

Look at the picture, *Return of the Prodigal Son.* The person who is looking straight ahead appears to be talking. The others appear to be listening. Think about the reason we listen to others.

WHAT TO DO: Match each type of talking with a reason for listening. Some reasons will be used more than once.

What We Say

_____ **1.** a joke

_____ **2.** directions to a doctor's office

_____ **3.** a recipe for cookies

_____ **4.** steps to fix a bike

_____ **5.** news about your cousin

_____ **6.** the page your homework is on

_____ **7.** a ghost story

_____ **8.** chores your parent wants you to do

Why We Listen

a. for enjoyment
b. to learn how to do something
c. to find something
d. to understand what someone expects
e. to learn about other people

Reading/Language Arts Objective: The student sets purposes for listening depending on the situation.

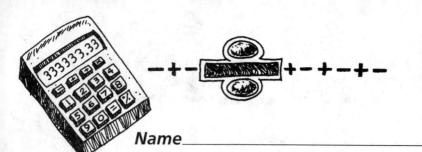

Name_____ Date_____

Number Patterns in Addition

In *Return of the Prodigal Son*, you see many repeating patterns. You can use patterns to help you solve math problems.

WHAT TO DO: Use the finger patterns to solve the math problems. Write the number sentences on the lines.

1.

_____ + _____ = _____
fingers   fingers   fingers

2.

_____ + _____ + _____ = _____
fingers   fingers   fingers   fingers

3.

_____ + _____ + _____ = _____
fingers   fingers   fingers   fingers

Mathematics Objective: The student uses patterns to identify strategies for addition and subtraction, such as doubles and near-doubles.

Name _____ Date _____

What Do You See?

Can you find a big eye in *Return of the Prodigal Son?* It reminds us that we use our eyes to observe the world.

A group of students went to the seashore. Their teacher told them to observe living things. Later, the teacher asked them to write about what they saw.

WHAT TO DO: Read what these students wrote. Then, answer the questions.

Jan: The place was full of smelly, dead fish. Yuck!

Ted: I saw two crabs. One was larger than the other. I saw lots of seagulls.

Liz: I liked the long stalks of grass. When I looked at the grass up close, I found a beautiful insect with lacy wings.

1. Who followed the teacher's instructions? _____

_____

Who did not? _____

2. Why do you think the descriptions were so different?

_____

_____

Science Objective: The student compares and contrasts his or her own observations with those of others.

Name _____ **Date** _____

What Makes a Leader?

In *Return of the Prodigal Son,* one person appears to be looking straight ahead. The other people looks toward that person. He seems to be the leader.

WHAT TO DO: Read about each person below. Think about who would be a good leader. Then, answer the questions.

Val is a very hard worker. He keeps his promises. Val has a difficult time making choices.

Jayne listens to others. She makes decisions quickly when she has all the facts.

Travis makes decisions quickly. He likes to tell other people what to do. He gets mad when anyone questions his ideas.

1. Who would be the best leader? _____

Why? _____

_____

2. Who would be the poorest leader? _____

Why? _____

_____

3. What other quality should a good leader have? _____

_____

Social Studies Objective: The student identifies qualities of a leader and a follower.

SOCIAL STUDIES

Name _____   Date _____

Write a Play

Study the three people in the picture, *Return of the Prodigal Son*. Imagine that one of the people is the father, and the other two are his sons. Another child is returning home after many years.

WHAT TO DO: Plan a play about the family. Why is the person coming home? How does the family feel? Tell what will happen in the beginning, middle, and end of your play. Then, write what the people will say, the dialogue, to begin the play.

What happens in your play?

Beginning: _____

_____

Middle: _____

_____

End: _____

_____

Dialogue:

_____

_____

_____

THE ARTS

Arts (Theater) Objectives: The student collaborates to select interrelated characters, environment, and situations for classroom dramatizations; The student improvises dialogue to tell stories and formalizes improvisations by writing or recording dialogue.

Name ______________________ **Date** ____________

Artists use different lines, shapes, and colors to create variety and interest in artwork.

WHAT TO DO: Create variety in a scene by using different lines, shapes, and colors.

1. Select from a variety of tools:
Draw a farm, underwater, desert, or other kind of scene. Think of objects—animals, plants, people, or things—that go together. Use different shapes and sizes.

2. Use the tool to add a variety of colors or textures to the shapes. Choose colors that relate to your scene.

Technology Objective: The student uses software programs with graphics to enhance learning experiences.

Name _____ Date_____

VOCABULARY WITH VARIETY

Artists use contrast in colors or shapes for variety in their artwork. If writers need to use the same idea over and over again, they will try to use different words that have almost the same meaning to give their writing more variety.

WHAT TO DO: Practice variety in writing as you complete each activity. In each sentence, find two words that mean almost the same. Write the words.

1. Just then, my mouth was parched. Has your mouth ever felt dry before?

_____

2. We jumped into the cold ocean water. It was quite a chilly experience.

_____

3. Horns blared in the traffic jam. All the angry drivers honked their horns.

_____

4. Dennis always gulps his food. Mom has told him that he swallows too fast.

_____

Now, write a sentence about a fire. Use two or more words that have almost the same meaning.

5. _____

Reading/Language Arts Objective: The student describes how the author's choices (words, dialogue, pacing) affect the text.

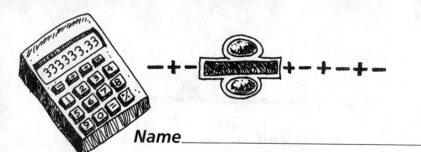

Name_____   Date_____

Circles and Squares

Kenneth Noland's painting *Split* is made up of squares and circles. Think how a square and a circle are different from each other.

WHAT TO DO: Fill out the chart. For each description, check the box to show whether it tells about a **Square** or **Circle.**

	Square	Circle
Straight lines		
Sharp points		
Curved lines		
Four sides		
No separate sides		

Now answer the questions.

1. What shape is good for rolling? _____

2. What shape is good for stacking? _____

Mathematics Objectives: The student identifies attributes of shapes and solids; The student uses attributes to describe how two shapes or two solids are different.

Name _____ **Date** _____

Use It Again

Kenneth Noland used shapes in his painting that have been used by thousands of other artists, but he used them in a new way. By *recycling,* we can use many common objects again and again, too. Recycling is a way we can save Earth's important resources.

WHAT TO DO: Solve each riddle. Choose a thing from the box. Write its letter on the blank beside the number.

a. colored newspaper comics
b. leaves that fall in autumn
c. cardboard box that a shirt came in
d. paper with old writing on one side
e. plastic bag from the bookstore

SCIENCE

_____ **1.** Cut me up and take notes on my clean side.

_____ **2.** Pile us on a garden bed to protect plants from winter winds.

_____ **3.** Use me as colorful wrapping paper.

_____ **4.** Wrap library books in me when it's rainy.

_____ **5.** Put gifts inside me for wrapping.

Your Idea
When you pull the last paper towel off a roll, a roller is left. On the back of this sheet, write an idea for using this roller.

Science Objective: The student designs ways to conserve materials that come from the earth; The student creates uses for recyclable materials.

Name_____   Date_____

Reading a Map

Artists use lines, shapes, and colors for variety. Mapmakers use lines, shapes, and colors to show information on maps.

WHAT TO DO: Study the map. Then, answer the questions. Write your answers on the back of this sheet.

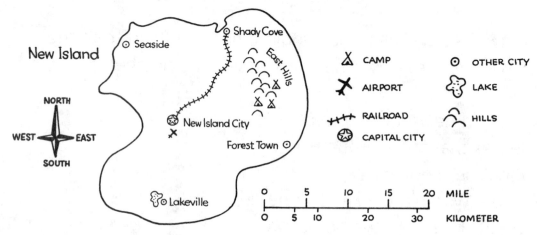

1. Is Shady Cove in the north or the south part of the island?

_____

2. Is Lakeville in the north or south? _____

3. What city has an airport? _____

4. Where are the campgrounds? _____

5. What is the capital city? _____

6. Circle the scale on your map. What is it used for? _____

_____

Social Studies Objective: The student uses symbols, finds locations, orients maps to determine direction, and uses scale to determine distance.

SOCIAL STUDIES

Name_____ Date_____

Contrast in the Arts

Artists sometimes create variety and contrast in their artwork. Dance, music, and theater use variety and contrast, too.

WHAT TO DO: Read the word boxes. Then, follow the instructions.

Dance Words	Music Words	Theater Words
tap dance	big horn sound	sad story
together	fast	many actors
apart	soft	evil character
slow	slow	a single actor
fast	loud	good character
ballet	little flute sound	happy story

1. Dance Words. Write two pairs of words that contrast.

a. _____   _____

b. _____   _____

2. Music Words. Write two pairs of words that contrast.

a. _____   _____

b. _____   _____

3. Theater Words. Write two pairs of words that contrast.

a. _____   _____

b. _____   _____

THE ARTS

Arts (Music) Objective: The student identifies similarities and differences in the meanings of common terms used in the various arts.

Name_____ **Date**_____

Artists use contrasting shapes and colors to create variety in artwork.

WHAT TO DO: Create variety in a design by using contrasting shapes and colors.

1. Select the ▭ or ◯ shape tool or the ➤ tool. Choose a geometric shape. Draw the same shape in different sizes.

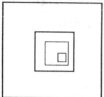

2. Create contrast. Use the 🖊 tool or the 🖌 tool to draw one different shape.

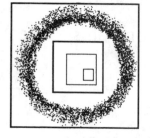 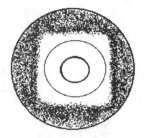

3. Select the 🪣 tool and add color. Use only warm or only cool colors.

Technology Objective: The student uses software programs with graphics to enhance learning experiences.

TECHNOLOGY

Name_____   Date_____

Writing Complete Sentences

A painting, such as *Touchwood Hills,* is complete when the artist has included everything he or she wants. A complete sentence must include a subject and a verb. The subject names the doer. The verb tells the action. A complete sentence also has end punctuation, such as a period, question mark, or exclamation mark.

WHAT TO DO: Read each sentence. If it is complete, put an **X** in the blank.

_____ **1.** I see a line of hills over there.

_____ **2.** The long, snaky fence

_____ **3.** Wheat is waving in the wind.

_____ **4.** I see many lines from left to right.

_____ **5.** Fence posts that have fallen over

_____ **6.** A very high hill is in the distance.

Now write two complete sentences of your own.

7. _____

_____

8. _____

_____

Reading/Language Arts Objective: The student composes complete sentences in written texts.

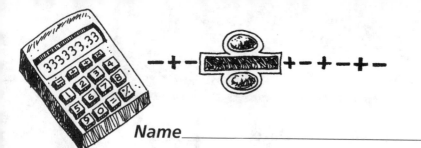

Name_____ Date_____

Math in Our World

What objects can you count in the painting? You can count the fence posts but not the stalks of grass. In the real world, it is easy to count some things but not others.

WHAT TO DO: Study each picture. Write **yes** in the corner box if the things are easy to count. Write **no** if they are not.

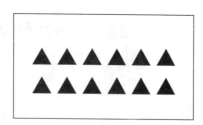

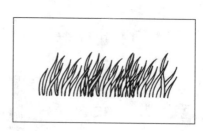

A. _____   **B.** _____

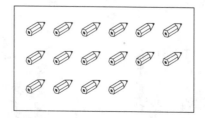

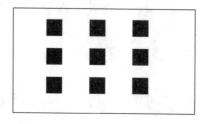

C. _____   **D.** _____

Check the statements that are true about the numbers of objects in the boxes.

_____ **1.**   A < B   _____ **2.**   A > C

_____ **3.**   B = C   _____ **4.**   C = E

Mathematics Objectives: The student relates informal language to mathematical language and symbols; The student identifies the mathematics in everyday situations.

Name _____ Date _____

Which Things Are Alive?

In a landscape painting like *Touchwood Hills,* there are pictures of many living things. There are also things that have never lived. Some nonliving things, such as wood in a fence, come from living things.

WHAT TO DO: In each picture row, cross out one thing that doesn't fit.

A.

B.

C.

1. Now look at all the pictures you crossed out. Are they all

living things? _____
2. Find three living things in the picture boxes. Write their

names. _____

SCIENCE

Science Objective: The student compares and contrasts biological and non-biological objects from the past and present (biological to biological, non-biological to non-biological, and biological to non-biological).

Name _____ Date _____

People Earn a Living

Look at the painting *Touchwood Hills.* The fence and the field might make you think of a farm. Farmers grow crops to sell so they can make a living. People sell other things to make a living, too. These are called *goods.* What does an artist sell? Some people don't sell anything to make money. Instead, they make a living with their skills or knowledge. They sell services.

WHAT TO DO: Look at each picture. Write **goods** if the person sells things to make a living. Write **services** if the person makes a living using skill or knowledge.

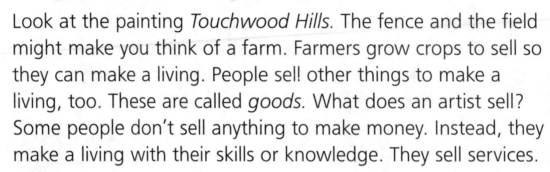

_____ _____ _____

On the back of this sheet, write about a job that interests you. Tell why.

Social Studies Objective: The student describes different ways people satisfy their needs and wants, past and present.

Name _____ **Date** _____

A DANCE AND A PAINTING

Use your imagination when you look at *Touchwood Hills*.
Here are some things you might see in the painting:

A long , low fence with a repeating pattern of fence posts.
Tall grass waving in the breeze.
A distant hill that is big and dark.

WHAT TO DO: Each number describes a dance step. Write
fence, grass, or **hill** in the blank to tell what the step
reminds you of. If the step does not remind you of the
painting, leave the blank empty.

_____ **1.** A heavy, slow dance, far back on the stage

_____ **2.** A dance in which dancers sway with their arms
     over their heads

_____ **3.** A clapping, stomping dance

_____ **4.** A line dance in which dancers hold hands and all
     do the same steps

_____ **5.** A group dance in which every dancer does
     something different

Now, choose one of the steps that reminds you of the painting.
Tell why that step is like the painting.

THE ARTS

Arts (Dance) Objective: The student responds to a dance using another art form and explains the connections
between the dance and his or her response to it.

Name _____ Date _____

Artists use similar colors to create harmony in artwork.

WHAT TO DO: Create harmony with color in an animal design.

1. Select from a variety of tools: ✏ 🖌 ▭ ◯ ╲
Draw the shape of an animal with a large body.

2. Draw lines across the body with the ╲ tool.

3. Create harmony with color. Select the 🖐 tool and three
or four harmonious colors.
Fill all the spaces with those colors.

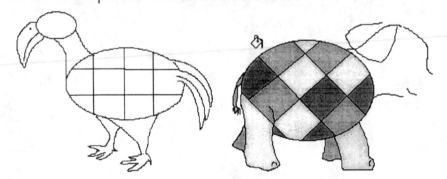

Technology Objective: The student uses software programs with graphics to enhance learning experiences.

TECHNOLOGY

204

Name_____ **Date**_____

Writing Safety Rules

Look at the painting of a hotel by Monika Steinhoff. Did you know that hotels have safety rules to protect their guests?

WHAT TO DO: Read these safety rules. Find three spelling errors in the safety rules. Cross out each misspelled word and write it correctly above the word.

Safety Rules in Your Home

a. Never play with matches.

b. Pick up toys and clothes so people don't trip.

c. Get your parents' help when you plug in soemthing.

d. Make sure your smok detectors work.

e. Make sure the handles of pans are over the stove. If they stik out, someone could get burned.

Write a safety rule. Use a complete sentence. _____

_____

_____

Reading/Language Arts Objectives: The student writes messages that can be read by others (for example, by spelling conventionally familiar and regular words); The student determines how one's own writing achieves its purposes.

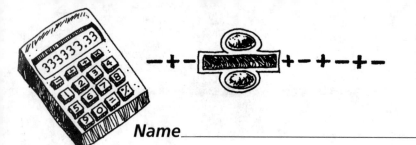

Name_____ Date_____

Telling Time

Pretend you are in the hotel painted by Monika Steinhoff. The lobby, or main room, has a big clock.

WHAT TO DO: Write the correct time for each item.

1.

_____

2.

_____

3.

_____

4.

_____

5. What is another way to name the time on clock 1?

_____

6. What time is it right now? Draw a clock face with hands to show the time.

Mathematics Objective: The student uses hours and minutes to describe the time shown on a clock.

Name _____ **Date** _____

Alike and Different

An artist might paint things that are nearly alike but also different. In this way, the artist gives harmony and variety to a picture. Many things in our world are nearly alike but not *exactly* alike.

WHAT TO DO: In each row, check the two objects that are most alike. Then, write how they are alike and how they are different.

Alike: _____

Different: _____

Alike: _____

Different: _____

Science Objective: The student sorts and analyzes objects according to like properties.

Name _____ Date _____

Think About Values

Look at the painting by Monika Steinhoff. Pictures on the tiles tell us about the people who made them. Pictures of animals and crops show that farming was important to these people. The designs on the chairs show how much they cared about beauty. People in every time and place have *values,* or things that are important to them.

WHAT TO DO: Each sentence states a value. Put a ✓ in the blank if you think your community and country have that value.

_____ **1.** Everyone has a right to vote.

_____ **2.** Everyone has a right to education.

_____ **3.** All people should have the same religion.

_____ **4.** We should help people in need.

_____ **5.** People have a right to say what they think about the government.

_____ **6.** The government should tell people what jobs to do.

_____ **7.** A big country has the right to take over a little country.

8. Now, write a sentence that tells about a value that you have.

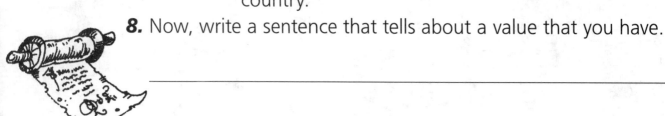

_____

_____

Social Studies Objective: The student examines changes in individuals, families, and communities over time such as change in beliefs, traditions, values, and knowledge.

SOCIAL STUDIES

Name _____ **Date** _____

A Stage Set for a Play

Find the people in the painting of the hotel by Monika Steinhoff. Do you think they feel warm, safe, and happy inside? Or do you feel closed in? Pretend you will put on a play about the people in the painting. You could make stage decorations to show the mood, or feeling, of the play. These decorations are called a *stage set*.

WHAT TO DO: Read each description of a stage set. On the blank, describe the mood of this play in a few words.

1. A lamp sheds warm, bright light. The room is full of

beautiful color. _____

2. Heavy, dark lines on the windows and doors look like bars in

a jail. _____

3. The room is dark. Some tiles have fallen off. Some windows

are cracked. _____

4. Now, choose the stage set you like the best. On the back of

this sheet, draw the stage set. _____

THE ARTS

Arts (Theater) Objective: The student visualizes environments and constructs designs to communicate locale and mood using visual elements (such as space, color, line, shape, texture) and aural aspects using a variety of sound sources.

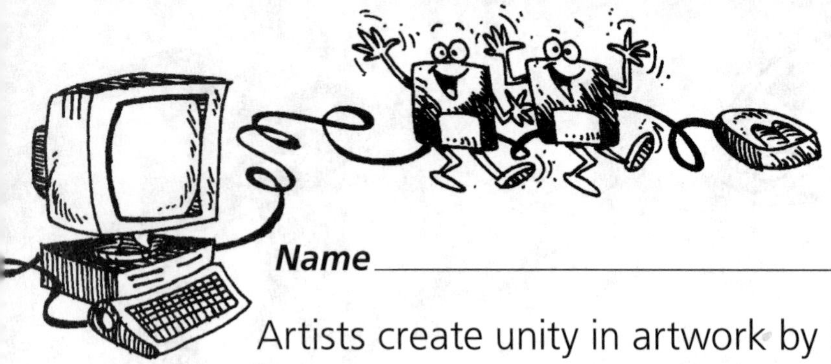

Name_____ Date_____

Artists create unity in artwork by balancing harmony and variety.

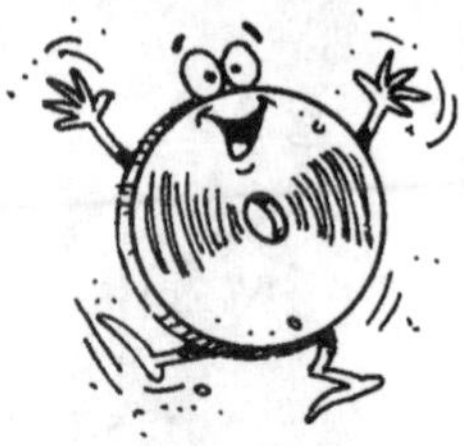

WHAT TO DO: Create a flag or banner that uses harmony and variety to show unity.

1. Select the ☐ tool and draw a large rectangle for a flag or banner.

2. Select the ✐ tool, the 🖌 tool, or the ＼ tool. Add a border. Use curved or straight lines.

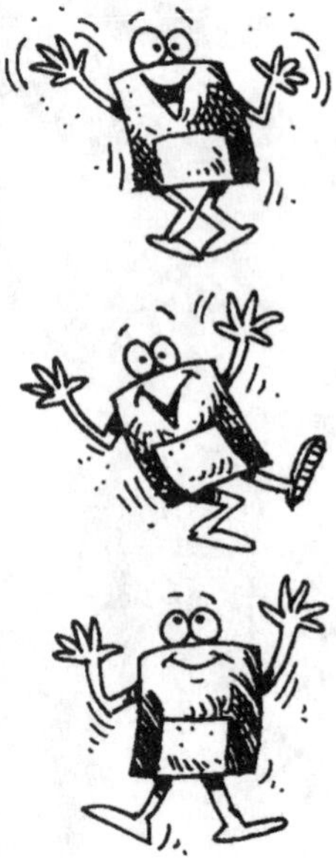

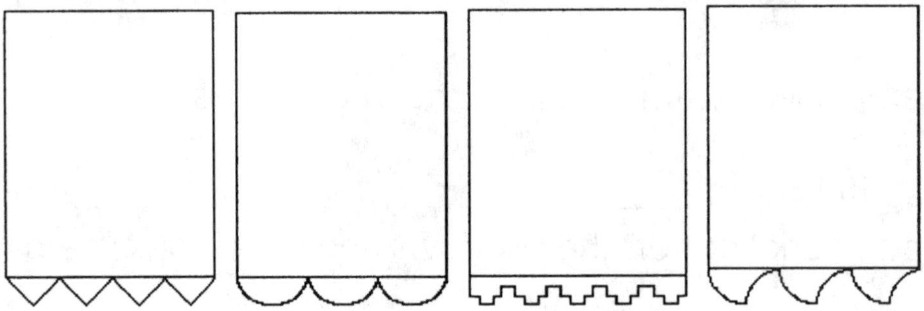

3. Choose your favorite season of the year. Create variety by drawing four different objects you think about during that season.
Select from a variety of tools: ✐ 🖌 ☐ ○ ＼

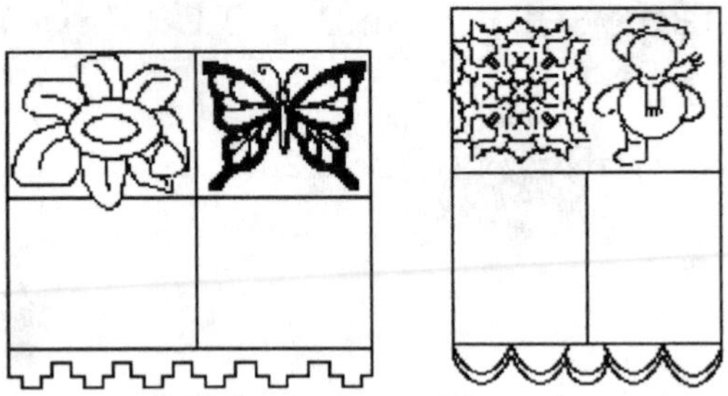

4. Create harmony with color. Choose about four hues to show the mood of the season.
Select from a variety of tools: 🖌 🪣 🖌 🔨

Technology Objective: The student uses software programs with graphics to enhance learning experiences.

TECHNOLOGY

*Name*_____ *Date*_____

Making Words Plural

Rick's class went to the art museum one day. Rick wrote about the trip. He might need help making some of his words plural, though. When a word is in its *plural* form, you know that it names more than one thing.

Rules for Forming Plurals

- For most words, add **-s.**
- If the word ends in **x, ch, sh, s,** or **ss,** add **-es.**
- Remember, some words don't follow the rules. For example, the plural of *child* is *children.*

WHAT TO DO: Help Rick with his plural words. Rewrite each sentence, making the underlined word plural.

1. Each wall was covered with picture. _____

_____

2. I counted 40 wall in the museum! _____

_____

3. I liked a drawing called *Two Fox.* _____

_____

4. We saw many photograph, too! _____

_____

5. All child liked the finger-paint display. _____

Reading/Language Arts Objective: The student uses conventions of grammar and usage (including subject-verb agreement, plurals, and verb tenses).

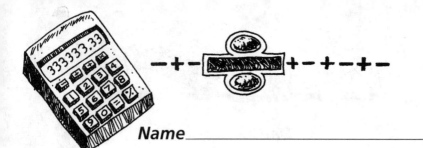

Name_____ Date_____

Facts in Graphs

The Guggenheim Museum is an art museum. Dana's class wanted to start an art museum at school. The children brought their art to school. This is what they had:

Art for Our School Art Museum

	Paintings	Drawings	Photographs	Sculptures	Other
10					
9					
8					
7					
6					
5					
4					
3					
2					
1					
0					

WHAT TO DO: Study the graph about the school's museum. Write the correct answer.

1. How many paintings does the museum have? _____

2. What is the next-largest group? _____

3. How many sculptures do they have? _____

4. How many drawings do they have? _____

5. What do you think "Other" means? _____

_____

Mathematics Objective: The student draws conclusions and answers questions based on graphed data.

Name_____   Date_____

ANIMAL ARMOR

Part of the Guggenheim Museum has a spiral shape. A spiral is a curved line that looks like water going down a drain. What else has a spiral shape? Think about a snail shell. The top part of the shell is a spiral. Many animals have an outside shell. The shell is a kind of armor that protects the animal. Other animals are protected by bones inside their bodies. Some animals have no shells or bones at all.

WHAT TO DO: Tell whether the animal has a shell of some kind, bones, or no shells or bones at all. Write the animal name in the correct box on the chart.

oyster	tiger	lobster	monkey	worm
crab	blue jay	giraffe	jellyfish	cat
eagle	beetle	pig	human	clam

Shell	Bones	Neither

Science Objective: The student observes differences in the structures and functions of plants and animals.

Name _____ Date _____

American Landmarks

The Guggenheim Museum is a landmark in New York. A landmark is an important place or building that helps us remember people or events in history.

WHAT TO DO: Study the map and then answer the riddles. Write the correct letter beside each number.

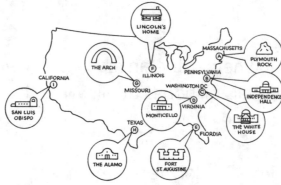

_____ **1.** Pioneers started west from here.

_____ **2.** I am Thomas Jefferson's home in Virginia.

_____ **3.** The Pilgrims landed here.

_____ **4.** I am a settlement in California.

_____ **5.** American independence was declared here.

_____ **6.** The president calls me "home."

_____ **7.** I am an old Spanish fort in Florida.

_____ **8.** I am a fort in Texas.

_____ **9.** I am Honest Abe's home in Illinois.

Social Studies Objective: The student explains the significance of various local, state, and historical landmarks.

Name _____ Date _____

Squares and Circles in Dance

The Guggenheim Museum has many circles and rectangles in its design. These patterns are exciting to look at. You can create an exciting dance by using the same idea of joining circles and squares.

WHAT TO DO: Which dance movement shows movement in a circle? Which shows movement in a square? Write **circle** or **square** on the blank below the picture.

A. _____ **B.** _____

Make up a dance for two dancers. Choose a "square" movement for one dancer and a "circle" movement for the other. How will the movements of the dancers go together?

Arts (Dance) Objective: The student explores, discovers, and realizes multiple solutions to a given movement problem, chooses a favorite solution, and discusses the reasons for that choice.

THE ARTS

Name _____ Date _____

Architects create unity in architecture by balancing harmony and variety in shapes and colors.

WHAT TO DO: Create unity by using both harmony and variety in the design of an art museum.

1. Use the ☐ or ⬭ shape tool or the ➤ tool to design the outside of an art museum with different geometric shapes.

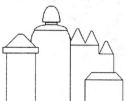 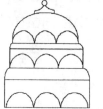 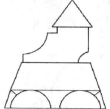

2. Show harmony by repeating the same shapes in different sizes for doors, windows, or other details.

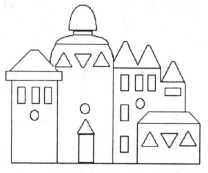

3. Use the ✎ tool to add color and texture. Select two or three colors and textures that match the mood of the building.

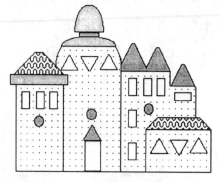

Technology Objective: The student uses software programs with graphics to enhance learning experiences.

TECHNOLOGY

Answer Key

UNIT 1, *Lesson 1*

Reading/Language Arts
1. zigzag
2. vertical
3. horizontal
4. diagonal
   Sentences will vary.

Mathematics
1. horizontal, vertical
2. horizontal, diagonal
3. curved
4. horizontal, vertical
   Students find and trace squares, circles, rectangles, and triangles in the picture of the sculpture.

Science
1. up
2. down
3. up
4. down
5. up
6. down

Social Studies
1. Color outline of Mexico on map.
2. Color outline of United States with different color.
3. south
4. Circle Pacific Ocean on map.
5. east

Arts (Dance)
1. curved
2. horizontal
3. vertical
4. diagonal
5. zigzag

Technology
Students will use drawing and painting programs to draw a place they know.

UNIT 1, *Lesson 2*

Reading/Language Arts
1. broken
2. thin
3. thick
4. rough
5. solid
6. smooth

Mathematics
2. 3, 9; 9
3. $2 + 2 + 2 + 2 = 8$; 8

Science
Circle goldfish, person, bird, tree, squirrel, and grass.

Social Studies
Urban: skyscraper, taxicabs, hotels, subway, traffic jams
Rural: rancher, crops, forest, farmer, ranger

Arts (Music)
Answers will vary.

Technology
Students will use drawing and painting programs to draw a variety of lines.

Answer Key

UNIT 1, *Lesson 3*

Reading/Language Arts
1. Webs will vary.
2. Poems will vary.

Mathematics
$\frac{1}{2}$, $\frac{2}{3}$, $\frac{3}{4}$, $\frac{1}{3}$, $\frac{1}{4}$

Science
Draw and label parts of a carrot.

Social Studies
notebook–paper; poster–paper;
napkin–paper; baseball bat–wood;
cardboard box–paper
Answers will vary but might include
    table, stairs, floors.
Answers will vary but might include
    newspaper, paper towels, milk or
    food cartons.

Arts (Theater)
1. Stories will vary.
2. Answers will vary.
3. Pictures will vary but should include
   poplar trees and show an attempt to
   represent the mood of the play.

Technology
Students will use drawing and painting
programs to draw a picture with calm
lines.

UNIT 1, *Lesson 4*

Reading/Language Arts
1. F
2. O
3. F
4. F
5. O
6. F
7. O
8. O
9. F
10. O

Mathematics
1. minute
2. hour
3. second
4.–6. Answers will vary but should be
    reasonable.

Science
1. a
2. c
3. a
4. b
5. b or c

Social Studies
A. 5
B. 1
C. 3
D. 4
E. 2

Arts (Dance)
Answers will vary.

Answer Key

Technology
Students will use drawing and painting programs to draw an active picture using diagonal, curved, and zigzag lines.

UNIT 1, *Lesson 5*

Reading/Language Arts
1. circles
2. triangles
3. rectangles

Sentences will vary.

Mathematics
check with art
1. square
2. rectangle.
3. 8
4. 5

Science
swordfish–fish; monkey–mammal; turkey–bird

Social Studies
1. a
2. a
3. b
4. a

Arts (Dance)
1.–3. Responses will vary
4. circle
5. triangle

Technology
Students will use drawing and painting programs to draw a picture using geometric shapes.

UNIT 1, *Lesson 6*

Reading/Language Arts
1. The puppet is from Indonesia.
2. Do you think the puppet has a big nose?
3. My friend Maya likes the puppet.
4. Does the puppet have ten toes?
5. Brad says the puppet is colorful.

Mathematics
2. 25¢, 10¢, 5¢, 40¢
3. 10¢, 10¢, 10¢, 1¢, 31¢
4. 25¢, 10¢, 1¢, 1¢, 37¢

Science
1. b
2. b
3. a
4. b

Social Studies
1. past
2. now
3. past

Arts (Theater)
Answers will vary.

Technology
Students will use drawing and painting programs to draw free-form shapes.

Answer Key

UNIT 2, Lesson 1

Reading/Language Arts
1. Sentences will vary but should give plausible description of Pantheon.
2. Students choose a contemporary or ancient setting for their story.
3. Students describe characters in their stories.
4. Students summarize the events of their stories in one sentence.

Mathematics
cone–ice-cream cone; party hat
cylinder–soup can; soda can
cube–gift box; child's block
sphere–baseball; ball of yarn

Science
Answers for chart will vary.
A standard, such as inches or centimeters, is better because it is always the same length.

Social Studies
1. post office
2. school
3. library
4. road
5. Answers will vary.

Arts (Theater)
1. c
2. a
3. c

Technology
Students will use drawing and painting programs to draw a building using geometric shapes.

UNIT 2, *Lesson 2*

Reading/Language Arts
1. Answers may vary. Possible answers: nose, ears, mouth, eyes, chin.
2. Letters will vary.

Mathematics
1. yellow
2. orange
3. pink
4. orange
5. yellow

Science
Answers will vary but could include:
Milk carton: Cut off bottom and use as funnel or make into a bird feeder.
Newspaper: Use as packing material when sending packages or wrapping gifts.
Plastic cup: Punch holes in bottoms and use as flowerpots for small plants.
Glass jar: Make a slit in top and use as a coin bank.

Social Studies
Circle picture of person planting a small pine tree. Mark an X on the person throwing a match on the ground. Sentences will vary.

Arts (Music)
Explanations will vary. Possible explanations:
1. quiet, slow, soothing; to relax the baby
2. fast, funny; to make people laugh
3. quiet, soothing; to calm patients
4. loud, exciting; so everyone can hear and to help emphasize the beat

Answer Key

Technology

Students will use drawing and painting programs to draw a free-form mask.

UNIT 2, *Lesson 3*

Reading/Language Arts

1. They're climbing out of a big box.
2. They look like they might feel sleepy.
3. Clowns usually do funny things.
4. Answers will vary.

Mathematics

Circle the caterpillar, pin, and paper clip. Mark X on the shoe, cowboy hat, brush, and notebook.

Science

Lawn sprinkler–Water the lawn less often.
Shower head–Take shorter showers.
Floating garbage–Keep litter out of lakes, streams, and rivers
Students' ideas about saving water will vary but could include turning off the water while washing hands or brushing teeth.

Social Studies

1. Rio Grande
2. Santa Fe
3. mountains
4. east
5. north

Arts (Dance)

1. up
2. slow
3. forward
4. Answers might include: sneezing, laying, climbing, leaning, stretching, looking.
5. Titles and explanations will vary.

Technology

Students will use drawing and painting programs to draw pictures of themselves as clowns.

UNIT 2, *Lesson 4*

Reading/Language Arts

1. Jamal at the Frog Pond
2. Sue Hull
3. Jake Jones
4. Answers will vary but should be reasonable.

Mathematics

A. 20
B. 70
C. 90
D. 40
E. 60
1. 20 F
2. 90 F
3. C
4. A or D
5. Students mark 30˚ on F.
6. Students mark 80˚ on G.

Answer Key

Science
1. Plants
2. Animals
3. Animals
4. Plants
5. Animals
6. Plants
7. Plants
8. Animals
9. Students circle stem, leaf, roots, flower; students underline legs, lung, stomach, fur, gills, feather.

Social Studies
Answers will vary but could include the following:
Clothes on floor: You could trip on them. You could lose something.
Clothes in hamper: Floor is clear. You probably won't lose anything.
Do homework: You'll learn more. You will probably get better grades.

Arts (Dance)
1.–4. Answers will vary.
5. Dances will vary.

Technology
Students will use drawing and painting programs to draw overlapping pictures of people playing.

UNIT 2, *Lesson 5*

Reading/Language Arts
Answers may vary. Possible answers:
1. many
2. many large
3. many large red
4. Sentence 3 gives the most information.

Mathematics
1. 1, 3, 13
2. 2, 6, 26
3. 3, 4, 34
4. 5, 2, 52
5. 2, 7, 27

Science
1. sun; sun; sun
2. air; air; air; air
3. water; water; water

Social Studies
Answers will vary.

Arts (Dance)
1. yes
2. yes
3. no
4. yes
5. no

Technology
Students will use drawing and painting programs to draw overlapping pictures in a still life.

Answer Key

UNIT 2, *Lesson 6*

Reading/Language Arts
1. C
2. Around one billion people live in India. It is the second largest country in the world in population.

Mathematics
Students complete bar graph as follows:
monkeys–3 blocks
tigers–2 blocks
goldfish–7 blocks
parrots–4 blocks
turtles–6 blocks
bears–1 block

Science
1. snake
2. rabbit
3. turtle

Social Studies
1. c
2. b
3. a

Arts (Theater)
Pictures and answers will vary.

Technology
Students will use drawing and painting programs to draw three-dimensional forms.

UNIT 3, *Lesson 1*

Reading/Language Arts
1. fact
2. fantasy
3. fantasy
4. fact
5. fantasy
6. fact
7. fact
8. fantasy
9. fantasy
10. fantasy

Mathematics
1. Both are made from straight lines. A square has four sides, while a triangle has three sides.
2. Both are made from straight lines. A pentagon has five sides, while a hexagon has six sides.
3. Both have four sides. The sides of a square are all the same length, while a rectangle's length and width may be different.

Science
bananas–yellow; cherries–red; shoes–Answers will vary.
blueberries–blue; apple–red, yellow, or green; corn–yellow
tomato–red or yellow; grass–green; lemons–yellow

Social Studies
Paragraphs will vary.

Arts (Dance)
Costumes will vary
1. flap arms.
2. hop, bend knees, bob head.

Answer Key

Technology
Students will use drawing and painting programs to paint with primary and secondary colors.

UNIT 3, *Lesson 2*

Reading/Language Arts
I don't like strawberry ice cream.
Yesterday my cat had kittens.
My house is small.
My cousin lives in Florida.

Mathematics
1. $3 + 3 = 6$
2. $2 + 2 + 2 = 6$
3. $4 + 2 + 4 = 10$

Science
1. Circle sun.
2. Circle candle.
3.–4. Pictures will vary but should distinguish clearly between a daytime and nighttime scene.

Social Studies
Photographs: clothing, cars, buildings
Book: number of people, mayor's name, percentage of children in school

Arts (Music)
1. Circle violin.
2. Circle trumpet.
3. Circle bass drum.
4. Circle bassoon.

Technology
Students will use drawing and painting programs to create designs filled with grays.

UNIT 3, *Lesson 3*

Reading/Language Arts
Pictures will vary but should include objects mentioned in the paragraph students read.

Mathematics
1. 3, 5, 7, 8
2. 4, 12, 14, 16,
3. 15, 25, 30, 35, 40
4. 6, 15, 18, 21, 24
5. 20, 25, 35, 40, 45, 50
6. 12, 14, 18, 20, 22
7. 7, 9, 10, 11, 12
8. 40, 50, 60, 70, 80
9. 10, 16, 18, 20, 22
10. 13, 14, 15, 17, 18

Science
fall, 3
summer, 2
spring, 1
winter, 4

Social Studies
Answers will vary.

Arts (Theater)
Answers will vary.

Technology
Students will use drawing and painting programs to create outdoor scenes showing a mood.

Answer Key

UNIT 3, *Lesson 4*

Reading/Language Arts

Dear Ted,

    Your friend Jerry called. Can you play baseball with him tomorrow at 1 o'clock? He said you can call him back until 7 o'clock tonight.

                         Ryan

Mathematics

1. >
2. =
3. =
4. <
5. <
6. >
7. <
8. <
9. >
10. >

Science

1. many different sizes
2. plants.
3. bottom
4. swim or crawl

Social Studies

1. red, white, blue
2. 13
3. 50

Arts (Music)

$\frac{1}{2}, \frac{1}{2}$; 1, 1, 1, $\frac{1}{2}, \frac{1}{2}, \frac{1}{2}, \frac{1}{2}, \frac{1}{2}, \frac{1}{2}$, 1

Technology

Students will use drawing and painting programs to create dark, moody scenes.

UNIT 3, *Lesson 5*

Reading/Language Arts

Answers will vary.

Mathematics

Answers will vary. Possible answers:

Less than a pound: gloves, cup, empty soda can, ink pen

About a pound: box of pasta, notebook, can of vegetables, package of rice or beans

More than a pound: bicycle, chair, vacuum cleaner, television set

Science

1. sun; corn; chickens; people
2. sun; grass; deer; mountain lions

Social Studies

Answers will vary.

Arts (Dance)

1. b
2. c
3. b

Technology

Students will use drawing and painting programs to create name designs with warm or cool colors.

UNIT 3, *Lesson 6*

Reading/Language Arts

Chart:

Responses will vary.

Answer Key

Mathematics
1. 3:15
2. 10:47
3. 5:22
4. 9:30
5. 6:10
6. 1:50

Science
1. Circle the notebook.
2. Circle the wagon filled with bricks.
3. Circle the tree.
4. Circle the elephant.

Social Studies
Students correctly label the United States, Canada, Mexico, and the state they live in.

Arts (Music)
Sounds and songs will vary.

Technology
Students will use drawing and painting programs to create landscape scenes with cool colors.

UNIT 4, *Lesson 1*

Reading/Language Arts
Answers will vary. Possible answers:
1. The lamp is swinging back and forth. The light keeps bouncing from wall to wall.
2. The musician saws away on the violin and taps his foot on the floor.
3. The dancers swirl to the pounding rhythm.

Mathematics
1. 2 + 2 + 2 + 2 = 8
2. 4 + 4 + 4 = 12

Science
1.–5. Answers will vary.

Social Studies
1. Answers will vary.
2. Possible answers: playing checkers or other games; singing, listening to someone play and instrument, or telling stories.
3. Answers will vary.

Arts (Music)
1. no
2. yes
3. no
4. no
5. yes
6. no
7. yes
8. no

Technology
Students will use drawing and painting programs to create designs showing movement with lines.

UNIT 4, *Lesson 2*

Reading/Language Arts
1. valley
2. brightens

Answer Key

Mathematics
1. yes
2. no
3. no
4. no
5. yes
6. yes
7. no
8. yes

Science
1. Possible answers: tree, shrub, grass (on hillsides), bush.
2. Possible answers: sky, star, mountain, hill, building or part of a building
3. I would see the buildings and the artificial light inside them.
4. Possible answer: It would see the tools we use.

Social Studies
Answers will vary. Possible answers:
electric light: home—easier for people to see; work—able to work at night
television: home—entertained and informed; work—communicate with others
cellular phone: home—calls from car or other outside places; work—call the office from car

Arts (Dance)
Answers will vary. Possible answers:
1. Hold long strips of a very light cloth behind or above my head as I walk fast or run. Hold my hands out and twirl my body as I dip and swoop.
2. Hold my hands up or out. Open and close them over and over again. Open and close my eyes over and over again.
3. Answers will vary.

Technology
Students will use drawing and painting programs to show movement with curving and swirling lines.

UNIT 4, *Lesson 3*

Reading/Language Arts
Rhyming words: wool and full
Lines with same rhythm: Baa, baa black sheep/Yes sir, yes sir

Mathematics
2. The numbers are 100 apart.
3. All the numbers use only the digit 1 and add a place value.
4. no pattern
5. The numbers are 200 apart in descending order.

Science
The wave pattern in the final box of each set should complete the pattern shown in the three boxes preceding it.

Social Studies
Answers will vary. Possible answers:
1. the scarcity of an object, the value the people in the culture place on it, the ease it which the object can be carried
2. beads, shells, food, rocks
3. They could trade or barter. They could work for the object.

Arts (Dance)
Dances will vary.

Answer Key

Technology
Students will use drawing and painting programs to create designs with visual rhythm.

UNIT 4, *Lesson 4*

Reading/Language Arts
1.–2. Answers will vary.

Mathematics
Circle: A curved line where every point is equidistant from the center. Students should list places where they could see a circle in their environment.
Rectangle: A shape that has two sets of sides which are parallel. Students should identify places in their environment where they can see rectangles.
Triangle: A shape having three sides. Students should indicate places in their environment where they can see triangles.

Science
1. bee
2. hummingbird
3. bee
4. hummingbird
5. bee
   Answers will vary. Students should mention that pollen sticks to the bee's body so that when the bee travels to another flower, the pollen is rubbed off there. This helps pollinate the flower so that the flower makes seeds. In retur the flower provides food, or nectar, for the bee.

Social Studies
Answers will vary. Possible answers:
Home: sheets, bedspreads, curtains, clothing of all sorts; wood furniture, wood materials in one's house (lumber, paneling, shingles), paper of all sorts; breakfast cereals, breads, rice, tortillas, apple (juice), orange (juice), peanut butter, fruits and vegetables of all sorts.
School: paper of all sorts, pencils, book bags (if made of cotton, wool, or cardboard), baseball bat, rubber soles in gym shoes, clothing worn to or used at school.

Arts (Music)
Answers will vary. In the student's original rhythmic pattern, look for the element of repetition. If the studentís rhythmic pattern exhibits no repetition, ask her or him to defend it.

Technology
Students will use drawing and painting programs to create designs with repeating motifs.

UNIT 4, *Lesson 5*

Reading/Language Arts
1. walk
2. big
3. rain
4. talk
5. like

Mathematics
5. square
9. triangles, 4

Answer Key

Science

Answers will vary. Possible answers:

Feather: a duster or sweeper, an ornament to wear, a quill pen, padding for a winter garment, stuffing for a pillow.

Branch: poles to support a roof for a shelter, a stick for a sport such as hockey or baseball (the bat), firewood, a tool for digging in the ground.

Leaf: a napkin, a wiper for a table or desk, play money, a hand fan, fuel for a small fire.

Yes.

Social Studies

Use any reliable world map or globe to check students' labeling.

Arts (Theater)

1.–6. Answers will vary.

Technology

Students will use drawing and painting programs to draw objects in nature with patterns.

UNIT 4, *Lesson 6*

Reading/Language Arts

1. She wasn't sure where her book was. She thought it might be on the grass.
2. Probably not. She probably didn't want to tell her mom about forgetting that she'd left her books outside.
3. Endings will vary but should provide a resolution to the problem.

Mathematics

26, 42, 17
Students should show 4 tens and 6 ones.

Science

A. 2, B. 4, C. 3. D. 1, E. 3, F. 4, G. 2, H. 1
Answers will vary.

Social Studies

A. 3
B. 2
C. 1
D. 4
George Washington

Arts (Theater)

Answers will vary. Possible answers:

1. Painted scenes of circus tent, trapeze, clowns; boxes or benches that look like bleachers.
2. Old-fashioned objects, such as spinning wheels, old clocks, lanterns and candles; painted scenes of horse & buggies, old-fashioned storefronts, stagecoaches, etc.
3. Painted scenes of barren, rocky land, dark sky; spaceship or shuttle, space suits.

Technology

Students will use drawing and painting programs to create box designs with visual patterns.

UNIT 5, *Lesson 1*

Reading/Language Arts

Sentences will vary.

Answer Key

Mathematics
1. hexagon
2. open "T"
3. oval
4. tree

Science
Living things: bird, daisy, turtle, apple, corn, puppy
Nonliving things: desk, shoe, pencil, table, fork, chair
Students' lists will vary.

Social Studies
1. encyclopedia
2. encyclopedia
3. map
4. dictionary
5. encyclopedia or map
6. map
7. encyclopedia
8. encyclopedia or map
9. encyclopedia

Arts (Theater)
Dialogues will vary.

Technology
Students will use drawing and painting programs to design containers with formal balance.

UNIT 5, *Lesson 2*

Reading/Language Arts
1. papyrus
2. sphinx
3. sarcophagus
4. a massive stone structure with a square base and four triangular sides that slope upward to a point, built as tombs by the ancient Egyptians
5. a person who copied or wrote letters, contracts, and other documents by hand

Mathematics
1. 9:25
2. 2:40
3. 9:55
4. 1:05
5. 12:10

Science
Answers will vary. Possible answers:
1. The sun gives heat and light.
2. The plants need light to grow.
3. The cow eats plants, including grass.
4. The children may eat meat from a cow.

Social Studies
Answers will vary. Possible answers:
1. Students should clean up after themselves following art class.
2. Students should be in classes when the bell rings.
3. Everyone in a car must wear a seat belt.
4. Wear a bicycle helmet.
5. Keep all pets on leashes.
6. Family members take turns speaking.

Answer Key

Arts (Dance)
1.–4. Answers will vary.

Technology
Students will use drawing and painting programs to draw sarcophaguses with symmetry.

UNIT 5, Lesson 3

Reading/Language Arts
1. fall; students underline leaves, turning colors, days, shorter, jacket
2. her birthday; students underline cake, sang, candles
3. at the movies; students underline Saturday afternoon, popcorn, seat
4. take a trip or visit her grandparents; students underline suitcase, plane ticket, Grandma, Grandpa

Mathematics
1. 25, 20, 15, 20, 30
2. fifth
3. third
4. 15

Science
Answers will vary. Possible answers:
1. Use a potholder. Stay away from the flame.
2. Wear a helmet. Ride with traffic. Use hand signals.
3. Look both ways before crossing the street. Don't talk to a stranger.
4. Stay in the bus seat. Don't put your arms out the window.
5. Don't jump or slide around. Step out carefully.

Social Studies
1. rural
2. urban
3. Answers will vary.

Arts (Dance)
2. stretch, wiggle, bend
3. Answers will vary.

Technology
Students will use drawing and painting programs to design symmetrical chairs.

UNIT 5, Lesson 4

Reading/Language Arts
1. astronomer
2. solarium
3. solar
4. solstice
5. asteroids

Mathematics
1. hundred thousands
2. ten millions
3. hundred millions
4. ten thousands
5. thousands
6. 160,000,000; 93,000,000; 239,000; 24,900; 7,900

Science
1. 1986
2. 1789
3. 2356
4. 1825
5. 1940

Answer Key

Social Studies
Answers will vary.

Arts (Theater)
Answers will vary.

Technology
Students will use drawing and painting programs to create artworks that look like stitcheries.

UNIT 5, *Lesson 5*

Reading/Language Arts
1. In the game tomorrow, Jason will play.
2. Outside the window, a cool breeze blew.
3. Clare made her bed before breakfast.
4. In the middle of the night, we heard a howl.
5. There was a small clock on the table.

Mathematics
1. $2 + 2 + 2 = 6$ or $2 \times 3 + 6$
2. $2 + 2 + 2 + 2 = 8$ or $4 \times 2 = 8$
3. $2 + 2 + 2 + 2 + 2 + 2 = 12$ or $2 \times 6 = 12$

Science
1. mountain
2. desert
3. waterfall
4. lake
5. river
6. canyon
7. cave
8. swamp
9. volcano
10. prairie

Social Studies
Descriptions will vary. sundial; to tell time

Arts (Theater)
1.–3. Answers will vary.
4. Pictures will vary.

Technology
Students will use drawing and painting programs to create designs that emphasize one area.

UNIT 5, *Lesson 6*

Reading/Language Arts
1. sticky, wet
2. furry
3. cold
4. hot
5. smooth
6. wet
7. Sentences will vary.
8. Sentences will vary.

Mathematics
Wednesday: 3 circles
Thursday: 4 circles
Friday: 5 circles
15
6 cans, 12 cans, 24 cans, 48 cans; 90 total cans

Science
Raccoon: eats fruit, nuts, other small animals
Both: hunts at night, uses front paws like fingers, mask-like face, lives in forests, furry body
Panda: eats bamboo

Answer Key

Social Studies
1. recycling
2. conserving
3. conserving
4. recycling
5. Possible answers: cans, newspapers, magazines, plastic

Arts (Music)
1. plucked, bowed, hit
2. blown
3. hit or shaken
   Stringed Instruments: violin, harp, guitar, piano
   Wind Instruments: trumpet, flute, tuba, saxophone
   Percussion Instruments: cymbals, drum, tambourine, triangle

Technology
Students will use drawing and painting programs to create mask designs with formal balance.

UNIT 6, *Lesson 1*

Reading/Language Arts
1. up
2. down
3. up
4. down
5.–6. Sentences will vary.

Mathematics
1. 5 + 5 = 10
2. 5 + 5 + 5 = 15
3. 5 + 5 + 5 + 5 = 20

Science
1. Pattern: tree, flower, flower, tree. Draw a flower.
2. Pattern: bird, bird, tree, bird. Draw a bird.
3. Pattern: sun, star, sun, star, star. Draw a sun.

Social Studies
The following rules should be marked:
2, 4, 8.
9. Answers will vary.

Arts (Music)
Answers will vary.

Technology
Students will use drawing and painting programs to create harmonious designs using similar shapes and colors.

UNIT 6, *Lesson 2*

Reading/Language Arts
1. a
2. c
3. b
4. b
5. e
6. c
7. a
8. d

Mathematics
1. 5 + 5 = 10
2. 5 + 5 + 5 = 15
3. 5 + 5 + 4 = 14

Answer Key

Science
1. Ted and Liz; Jan
2. Answers will vary.

Social Studies
1. Jayne, because she makes decisions based on all of the facts.
2. Travis, because he gets angry when people disagree with him.
3. Answers will vary.

Arts (Theater)
Plays and dialogues will vary.

Technology
Students will use drawing and painting programs to draw scenes with a variety of lines, shapes and colors.

UNIT 6, *Lesson 3*

Reading/Language Arts
1. parched, dry
2. cold, chilly
3. blared, honked
4. gulps, swallows
5. Sentences will vary.

Mathematics
Square: straight lines, sharp points, four sides
Circle: curved lines, no separate sides
1. circle
2. square

Science
1. d
2. b
3. a
4. e
5. c
Ideas will vary.

Social Studies
1. north
2. south
3. New Island City
4. East Hills
5. New Island City
6. The scale is used to indicate mileage.

Arts (Music)
1. fast/slow, together/apart, tap dance/ballet
2. big horn sound/little flute sound, fast/slow, loud/soft
3. sad story/happy story, many characters/a single actor, evil character/good character

Technology
Students will use drawing and painting programs to create designs using contrasting shapes and colors.

UNIT 6, *Lesson 4*

Reading/Language Arts
Items 1, 3, 4, and 6 should be marked.
7.–8. Sentences will vary.

Answer Key

Mathematics
A. yes
B. no
C. yes
D. yes
Statement 1 is true.

Science
A. Cross out sun.
B. Cross out lightbulb.
C. Cross out porcupine.
1. no
2. Answers will vary.

Social Studies
A. services
B. services
C. goods
D. services
E. services
F. goods
Answers will vary.

Arts (Dance)
1. hill
2. grass
3. hill
4. fence
5. (empty)
Answers will vary.

Technology
Students will use drawing and painting programs to create animal designs with harmony.

UNIT 6, *Lesson 5*

Reading/Language Arts
c. soemthing something;
d. smok smoke;
e. stik stick
Sentences will vary.

Mathematics
1. 11:40
2. 3:35
3. 6:10
4. 2:30
5. twenty minutes before twelve
6. Answers will vary.

Science
Students check moon and sun. Possible answers:
Alike: They are part of Earth's orbit; they are in the sky; they shine.
Different: The sun makes its own light; the moon reflects light. The sun always looks the same; we see the moon in different phases.
Students check tractor and car. Possible answers:
Alike: They both are means of transportation, they both have wheels.
Different: A car is used on roads; a tractor is used on land. A car usually has a front and back seat; a tractor has only a front seat.

Social Studies
Students check sentences 1, 2, 4, and 5.
8. Answers will vary.

Answer Key

Arts (Theater)
Answers will vary. Possible answers:
1. happy, homey, cheerful, fun
2. lonely, scary
3. scary, unhappy, frightening
4. Pictures will vary.

Technology
Students will use drawing and painting programs to create banners or flags that use harmony and variety to show unity.

UNIT 6, *Lesson 6*

Reading/Language Arts
1. pictures
2. walls
3. Foxes
4. photographs
5. children

Mathematics
1. 10
2. photographs
3. 2
4. 4
5. Answers will vary. Possible answers: weavings, quilts, pieces of pottery, baskets.

Science
Shell: oyster, crab, beetle, lobster, clam
Bones: eagle, tiger, blue jay, giraffe, pig, monkey, human, cat
Neither: jellyfish, worm

Social Studies
1. G
2. D
3. A
4. I
5. B
6. C
7. E
8. H
9. F

Arts (Dance)
A. circle
B. square
Answers will vary

Technology
Students will use drawing and painting programs to create designs of art museums showing unity by balancing harmony and variety.

Teacher Notes

Teacher Notes

Teacher Notes

Teacher Notes